Please read and pass it on.

[illegible signature]

To Tax or To Ration:

Medicare, Medicaid, and Our Long-Term Healthcare Crisis

Dedications

To my mother, Loretta Mayer Doyle, whose tortured last years gave impetus to this book

Ken Doyle

To my elderly clients and their families who have already dealt with, or are currently grappling with, these issues

Larry Houk

To Tax or To Ration:

Medicare, Medicaid, and Our Long-Term Healthcare Crisis

Ken Doyle, PhD, and Larry Houk, JD

Old Stone House Publishers, Inc.
St. Paul, Minnesota

Old Stone House Publishers, Inc.
1611 West County Road B, Suite 315
Roseville MN 55113

Library of Congress Control Number 2009935529
ISBN Number 978-0-9842443-0-0

Cover Design by Chris LaVine
Cover Photo Credit: Mary Hope

Printed in the United States of America
by Highlight Printing, Minneapolis

10 9 8 7 6 5 4 3 2 1

Table of Contents

Part III: To Tax or To Ration –

Healthcare Rationing Is Here, and It's Expanding

Part IV: Foundation for a National Conversation –

Toward a Distinctly American Rationing Plan

List of Tables and Figures, with Sources

Table 6-3: Annual Private-Pay Nursing-Home Charges by Region
Centers for Disease Control, USDHHS, Compiled by Elderweb. Adapted by the Authors.

Table 6-4: How Do Nursing Home Residents Pay for Care?
National Nursing Home Survey (2004).

Table 16-1: Select Factors that Contribute to Soaring LTC Costs
By the Authors.

Preface

This book is about you, your mother, your dad, your grandmother, or perhaps an older sibling or your aging in-laws -- anybody you know who's likely to need long-term healthcare in the foreseeable future.

To put it bluntly, our American system for providing healthcare for our aging relatives, friends, and neighbors is simply not sustainable. The dollar figures – millions, billions, trillions – are so large that we can barely grasp them. The funding is so complex that we can hardly comprehend it.

The one thing that's clear is that we need to do *something*. As President Obama and many others have said recently, the status quo – doing nothing – is not an option.

But proponents of healthcare reform are proposing -- with remarkable optimism -- to eliminate hundreds of billions of dollars in fraud and waste from Medicare and Medicaid, and use those savings to fund a new health insurance program. Radio and TV ads are telling us how good the new program will be for us, and carefully deployed missionaries to Sunday morning talk shows are vigorously proclaiming every advantage and dodging every disadvantage. Opponents are countering with their own ads and emissaries. The airwaves are alive with exaggeration and distortion, if not outright deceit.

Few of the ads or emissaries are talking about *long-term* healthcare, how the proposed programs will help take care of America's growing numbers of frail elderly. When long-term care does enter the conversation, it's usually in the context of cutting back on the key programs.

It's all happening so fast. What's lacking is a calm, systematic discussion of the many problems with the current systems and the strengths and weaknesses of each possible solution. We don't care if the debate is dispassionate or passionate; we only care that it's reasoned, honest, and thorough.

We've written this book to provide the structure and some of the key resources for serious and free-ranging conversation about long-term healthcare for aging Americans. We envision book clubs and discussion groups around the country making their way through it, chapter by chapter, arguing to a consensus and then sending their considered opinions to their Senators and Representatives in Washington and their respective state capitals. While we certainly have our view of what long-term care should look like – and will present that view to stimulate discussion – what really matters is not that you agree with us but that you come up with your own views and share those views with our elected representatives.

To keep the discussion honest, we've tried hard to be non-partisan. There are some ideas here that will annoy Republicans, some that will annoy Democrats, and some that will probably annoy everybody. But we're convinced that the best solutions emerge when all relevant ideas are on the table.

We've also tried hard to avoid sensationalism. Healthcare is an easy topic to demagogue, and a little demagoguery goes a long way.

We're keenly aware of how much there is to read on this topic, and how little reading time many people have. So we've written this book on three levels. Depending on the time available, you can read it:

In the usual way, page by page, right through the Endnotes and Appendixes;

In the fashion of a condensed book, reading the "recapitulation" chapters and especially the "Grand Summary and Recommendations";

In the "Cliff's Notes" version, skimming just the boxed comments and factoids that appear systematically throughout the book.

Please forgive a certain repetitiveness as we recapitulate from time to time.

However you read it, we hope you will gather together some friends and relatives who have a stake in long-term healthcare, and begin the conversation.

We want to thank our friends and colleagues who read parts or, in some cases, all of the manuscript and offered brilliant recommendations, nearly all of which we happily accepted: Cheri Anderson, O.J. Doyle, Ken Michaelis, Leif Solberg, M.D., Pat Strother, Dan Sullivan, and Bill Wells. We want to be clear, however, that their commenting on the manuscript doesn't necessarily mean they endorse any or all of it. Any errors, gaps, or other insufficiencies are entirely our own doing.

At the same time we want to thank our student assistants: Researcher Adam Almen, Marketing Assistant Whitney Johnson, and Web Designer Denise Rath.

Finally, we want to thank the good folk at Highlight Printing, Minneapolis, for their ceaseless help and encouragement: Lisa Bickford, President, Chris LaVine, Creative Department, and the entire staff.

Ken Doyle
Larry Houk
St. Paul
9/11/2009

Part I
Medicare and Medicaid --
These Two Mainstays Are *Everybody's* Problem

Chapter 1

What We Want to Accomplish, and Why

Emily's Story

Emily and her husband had thought they were in pretty good shape. Nice house and cars, a couple of expensive vacations every year, membership in a respectable country club. When Albert died, he left an estate on the order of $500,000, along with instructions that whatever Emily didn't need would eventually be divided equally among their three children. Things changed dramatically when Parkinson's forced Emily into a nursing home at 78. In seven years at just over $75,000 a year, their entire estate disappeared – the house, the cars, their savings and investments, everything, even the bequest for the kids. Emily spent her last few years on Medicaid, confused, depressed, and frightened.

Federal Facts about Medicare and Medicaid

Fact: More than 45 million American Seniors depend on Medi*care* to pay their healthcare expenses. But the Medicare Board of Trustees predicts that Medicare will go broke in 2017.[1]

Fact: Congress has been borrowing from the Medicare Trust fund for years. The debt amounts to about $38 *trillion*.[2]

That's $124,000 for every man, woman, and child in the U.S. Payments on the loans are scheduled to start in 2027,[3] but nobody has any idea where the money will come from.

Fact: Medi*caid*'s nursing-home program pays the expenses for nearly three-quarters of a million elderly and disabled people. Of these, 76% are women; 60% are widowed, divorced, or single; and 53% are over 85.[4] The over-85 demographic is the fastest-growing segment of American society.

Fact: Approximately 38% of people who go into a nursing home are Medicaid-eligible the day they enter. Another 4% go onto Medicaid in roughly a year, when their personal assets are totally depleted, the rest in another two years.[5]

This is your mother we're talking about, or your grandmother; or maybe your dad or an aging in-law or older sibling.

It gets worse.

State Facts

Fact: Medicaid is funded roughly half by the federal government, half by the states. The states' shares are a far bigger percentage of their healthcare budgets than the federal share is of the federal healthcare budget. Medicaid is becoming a crushing burden on the states.[6]

Fact: As the states scramble to find ways to handle their Medicaid obligations, at least one governor has proposed that states stop paying nursing home expenses.[7] Imagine the turmoil as nursing homes all over the country close, and families try to find ways to take care of Grandma at home.

Fact: It's only a matter of time before the governors of 30 states remember that their legislatures have already enacted "filial responsibility" laws that can force adult children to take care of their parents' medical expenses, including what Medicaid has been paying for nursing home care.[8]

Fact: The first wave of the 77-million-member Baby

Boomer Generation is already starting to retire. They will all go onto Medicare as soon as they hit 65. If past behavior is any indicator, nearly half of that 77 million - 38.5 million! - will eventually need nursing home care. Absent major changes, virtually all of those who stay in the home for three or more years will use up all their personal assets and go onto Medicaid.

Family Facts

Fact: The average annual nursing home charge just passed the $78,000 mark, half that in some localities, double in others.[9] These charges are paid from the patient's own assets until those are depleted, then mainly by Medicaid. Private resources and long-term care insurance cover only a small percentage of the cases.

Fact: The average stay in a nursing home is about four years, but increasing numbers of patients with Alzheimer's, Parkinson's, diabetes, and other slowly debilitating diseases can be expected to spend ten, fifteen, even twenty years in nursing homes, all paid by Medicaid.

Fact: Most Seniors run out of money in about three years, and suffer the emotional upheaval you'd expect from insolvency combined with personal vulnerability. Thereafter they depend on *medical welfare* – Medicaid – and whatever indignity that dependence might carry for them.

Politics

Fact: Some healthcare reform advocates are proposing to withhold the annual Medicare payment increases usually paid to nursing homes, and to take away *hundreds of billions* of dollars from these programs to fund a new national health insurance program.[10]

Fact: While some sort of national health insurance program may be the only way to slow the increase in over-all healthcare costs, funding it with Medicare and Medicaid dollars seems more political than economic. It shifts healthcare dollars from elderly and disabled Americans to uninsured Americans and other U.S. residents. It represents no real savings, only a shift in priorities.

Purpose of This Book

Congress and the Administration are pushing for speedy healthcare reform. With all due respect, we submit that more important than swiftness is quality, and that quality reform is best accomplished by involving the American people in frank and open discussion.

> *More important than swiftness is quality, and quality is best accomplished through frank and open conversation with the American people.*

The purpose of this book, then, is *to start a national conversation about long-term healthcare for aging Americans.*

We want to sound the alarm about this neglected stepchild of today's health-care debate.

We want people in libraries, schools, and churches, in clubrooms, barbershops, and bars, in kitchens, living rooms, and back yards around the country to begin to talk seriously about how to pay for healthcare for our parents and grandparents, our older siblings, our aging in-laws – all the people in our lives who are struggling with, or will someday struggle with, long-term physical, emotional, and cognitive disabilities and diseases like Alzheimer's, Parkinson's, ALS, diabetes, or just plain growing really old.

Why? Because long-term healthcare is the 600-pound gorilla in the middle of the healthcare debate. Everybody knows it's there, but nobody's talking about it. It's too scary.

We want print, broadcast, and Internet reporters and editors, talk-show hosts and bloggers, and religious, civic, and political leaders to put *long-term* healthcare on the public agenda before it's too late.

Why? Because, according to *The Economist*, Medicare, Medicaid, and Social Security are mortgaged up to their ears.[11] It would take the total value of all the goods and services produced in this country (Gross Domestic Product) for the next five years to make good on promises already made, that is, a 100% tax on every individual's and company's income. Obviously that can't happen.

> *If Congress doesn't include long-term healthcare in its healthcare plan, we won't have a healthcare plan at all.*

Can it?

Most of all, we want people to communicate their views to their senators and representatives in Washington and in state capitals around the country.

Why? Because if Congress doesn't include *long-term* health-care in its healthcare plan, we won't have a healthcare plan at all.

Overview of the Book

To that end – promoting the national conversation – we're going to talk about Medicare and Medicaid, the principal programs that pay for long-term healthcare; about the trends that are threatening these programs' very existence; and about what we as a nation are going to have to do to salvage them while at the same time maintaining what's arguably the best healthcare in the history of the world.

Medicare (the government's healthcare program for Seniors) and Medicaid (the program for the poor) are both important to everybody who joins this conversation. Medicare pays every Senior's health, hospital, doctor, and prescription-drug expenses – but it's running out of money. Medicaid pays (among many things) just about everybody's nursing-home expenses if they stay in the home more than a few years. It's running out of money faster.

The three trends that are pushing Medicare and Medicaid to the brink are:

- More aging people making demands on the programs
- Increasing difficulty finding and keeping front-line care-givers
- Rising costs of everything medical.

In addition to looking at these trends in detail, we'll examine the consequences long-term care patients and their families suffer as a result of rising costs and falling services, and we'll explore the reasons why healthcare is so expensive.

When you run out of money, you have two choices: You can go get some more, or you can cut back on your spending. In healthcare terms, those choices translate into taxation or rationing.

> *The question is,*
> *To tax or to ration.*
> *The answer is,*
> *To tax and to ration.*

There's no doubt in our minds: It will be impossible to fix the American healthcare finance system simply by adding revenues, that is, raising taxes, especially if we intend to tax only the rich, or even the rich and the middle classes.

The alternative is "cost containment" – which often though not always is code talk for *rationing*.

There is no other practical alternative. Getting rid of fraud and inefficiency would surely help – if it could be accomplished. Getting the insurance companies and drug companies to reconsider their pricing would certainly be a step in the right direction. Persuading Americans to exercise more, reduce their salt, fat, and sugar intake, and wear their seatbelts would reduce our front-end healthcare costs but could worsen the problem by causing some people to live longer and spend more time in nursing homes. Living healthfully probably gives you more days, but likely more days at the frail end of your life than in the robust middle.

Rationing is already with us. We'll talk about rationing as it's already being practiced, and we'll talk about the more drastic kinds of rationing that are waiting round the bend.

We know that many people hate the very idea of rationing. But we can't have an honest discussion of all the options without taking a good look at what various people mean by rationing, and what's good and bad about each.

The fundamental question is, "To Tax *or* to Ration." The answer will surely be "To Tax *and* to Ration." The only question is, How much of each? The fundamental purpose of this book is to get people to debate this question and communicate their views to Washington.

Chapter 2

Medicare and Medicaid

We all know that long-term healthcare is amazingly expensive. The costs are paid partly out of pocket but mainly through Medicare and Medicaid. Medicare is the government's healthcare program for older Americans. Medicaid has two parts: The part most people know about, namely acute healthcare for the nation's poor; and the less familiar part, the part that pays nursing home expenses for the majority of nursing-home patients around the country.

> *Everybody's talking about Medicare but nobody's talking about Medicaid.*

Although both Medicare and Medicaid should be central parts of the healthcare debate, everybody's talking about Medicare but almost nobody's talking about Medicaid. Worse yet, when people do talk about Medicaid, it's usually in the context of taking money away from it in order to fund a national health insurance program.

Medicare

Just a little refresher to make sure we're all on the same page: Medi*care* is the government's medical program for

Seniors, the familiar Part A, Part B, Part C, and Part D programs people sign up for when they turn 65.[1]

Medicare (along with Social Security) is funded by a payroll tax on employers and employees, including the self-employed. Any tax money not used in a given year is accumulated in a trust fund that's supposed to be invested to pay future benefits. But Congress has been borrowing from that trust right along, so quite a few people worry that the trust-fund money might not be readily available when it's needed.[2] Congress is supposed to start paying back those loans in 2027.

Medicare is for Seniors' *acute* health care, the accidents and illnesses we encounter in everyday life, the cuts and burns and breaks, the hospitalizations, drugs, and treatments, the operations and other medical procedures – the whole kit and caboodle of health ills and remedies we all experience.

Figure 2-1: Federal Spending 1962-2082 as Percent of GDP

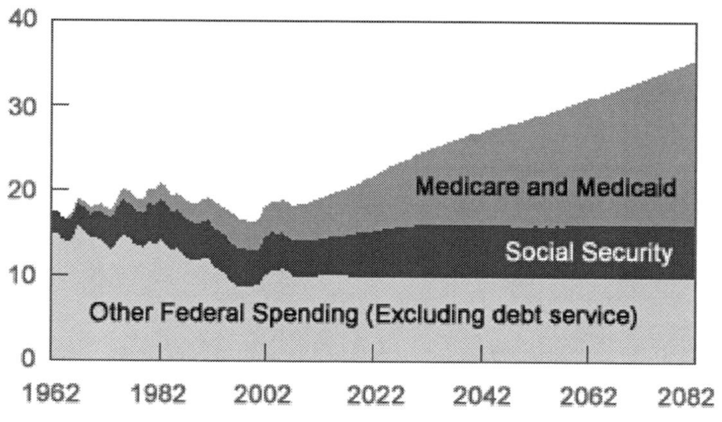

Source: Congressional Budget Office (2009)
http://www.cbo.gov/publications/collections/health.cfm

Medicare does not pay for custodial care anywhere – not at home, not in an assisted-living center, not in a skilled nursing facility or anything in between.

Medicare will pay for short-term convalescent care if you go straight from a hospital to a nursing home. But *it won't pay the long-term costs for people who have to move into a nursing home because they just can't take care of themselves or have developed a debilitating disease like Alzheimer's, Parkinson's, or ALS.*

Medicaid

In contrast, Medi*caid* is the government's medical program for the poor.[3]

But it's much more than that. It's what pays most people's nursing home costs once they've spent all their savings, cashed in their investments, signed over their retirement funds, and sold the house and other assets. In short, it's what takes over when virtually all personal assets have been depleted.

Medicaid, unlike Medicare, doesn't have a trust fund. It's simply a general budget item paid jointly by the federal government and the individual states. Accordingly, it's far more vulnerable than either Medicare or Social Security.

Medicaid covers the whole range of health-care needs for people who meet their state's strict definitions of poverty. Lots of people don't like the term, but it's *medical welfare*.

Why should middle- and upper-middle-class Americans care about medical welfare?

Because just about every middle and upper-middle class American who goes into a nursing home for long-term care is going to be poor sooner or later – probably sooner.

More than half the people in this country over 65 are going to land in a nursing home some time or other. Almost a third of them will stay three months or more, a quarter will stay a year or more, and one in eleven will stay five years or more.[4]

The Kaiser Foundation (2006) found that 38% of nursing-home residents are Medicaid-eligible at admission.[5] Another Kaiser study (2007) found that 76 percent of nursing-home residents are female, 60% of those are single, and 55% of those are over age 85.[6] These are the very people least able to pay their own way. Nearly all of them will exhaust their personal assets within three years.

Table 2-1: How Do Nursing Home Residents Pay for Care?

	Population	Personal	Medicare	Medicaid	Other
All	1,492,200	255,300	118,400	875,300	54,400
< 65	174,900	10,200	7,100	119,800	10,800
65-74	174,100	16,700	14,800	110,900	7,600
75-84	468,700	72,400	44,300	267,700	17,700
>85	674,500	156,000	52,200	376,900	18,300
Male	430,500	69,400	36,900	230,500	25,100
Female	1,061,700	185,900	81,400	644,800	29,300
White	1,276,000	246,800	105,100	717,400	47,100
Black	186,100	5,700	11,000	136,800	6,200

Source: Extracted from: National Nursing Home Survey (2004).
Not enough Asian and Latino cases in the sample for reliable estimates.

On top of that, some people – those with Alzheimer's, Parkinson's, ALS, diabetes, and other debilitating diseases -- may linger for years, even decades. Yet another Kaiser Foundation study (2004) found that 69% of newly admitted residents are sicker than the cohort that preceded them.[7]

At $6,500 *a month* on average, nobody we know has enough money to last for more than a few years, even after they liquidate everything and give up any hope of leaving something to the kids, the grandkids, and maybe a favorite charity.

Fully 80% of all nursing-home patient-days are paid by Medicaid.

Fully 80% of all nursing-home patient days are paid by Medicaid.[8] In maybe seven or eight years, there simply won't be enough money to do what needs to be done.

The only way to keep Medicaid solvent will be to raise taxes dramatically – or cut benefits ruthlessly. The problem is, neither the public nor the economy would ever tolerate taxes high enough to keep the program solvent. That's why we say rationing is inevitable.

Why Should *You* Worry about Medicaid?

The first reason you should worry about Medicaid is that the more money it pays out the higher your taxes will go to cover the expenditures.

The other reason is that you, your parents, or your grandparents are probably going to need long-term care some day. If so, odds are that they, or you, won't have enough personal assets to pay the cost and will wind up on Medicaid too -- if it still exists.

To summarize, Medicare and Medicaid are the mainstays of the American system of long-term healthcare, Medicare because it pays Seniors' acute healthcare expenses, Medicaid because it pays their nursing home charges. Both programs are in peril, especially Medicaid, but few people in authority are talking about these problems. Whether the eventual outcome is to increase your taxes or ration your healthcare or both, you have an important stake in both these programs.

> *Whether the eventual outcome is to increase your taxes, ration your healthcare, or both, you have an important stake in both Medicare and Medicaid.*

Chapter 3

First Recapitulation

To millions of older and soon-to-be-older Americans, Medicare and Medicaid are too important to neglect. Once people turn 65, they depend on Medicare for their routine and extraordinary medical needs.

No surprise there.

What is a surprise to many people is that Medicaid, the healthcare program for the poor, has become also the healthcare program that pays the nursing home expenses for better than half the nursing home residents around the country.

These are huge programs, and they're both in danger.

People who need nursing home care have little choice but to turn to Medicaid. Medicare pays virtually nothing toward long-term nursing-home expenses; nor does regular health insurance. Long-term care insurance is expensive, and has yet to prove itself. Only the wealthy can pay long-term care expenses out of their own pockets.

That leaves Medicaid.

The people for whom Medicaid pays are those whose entire fortunes – house, car, savings, investments, bequests – have already been liquidated to pay nursing-home expenses. Only after that money's gone does Medicaid step in.

At $6,500 a month, it takes on average about three years to deplete a family's fortune.

Another troubling fact is that laws on the books in 30 states – as yet unenforced – stipulate that adult children can be required to pay their indigent parents' healthcare expenses. In other words, if Mom goes onto Medicaid, the laws are already in place to force you to reimburse the program for whatever it spends on her behalf.

Here's why the problem is so pressing:

Both Medicare and Medicaid are teetering on the brink, Medicare on the brink of bankruptcy, Medicaid on the brink of insufficiency. The latest government estimate is that Medicare will go insolvent in 2017. Medicaid will probably run out of money before that.

With the notable exceptions of Senator Kohl and his "Confidence in Long-Term Care Insurance Act of 2009," Senator Kennedy and his "Community Living Assistance Services and Support (CLASS) Act," Senators Gregg and Conrad and their "Bipartisan Task Force for Responsible Fiscal Action Act," and Senator Klobuchar and her "Americans Giving Care to Elders (AGE) Act," you can count on the fingers of one hand the members of Congress or representatives of the Administration who are talking about the importance of Medicare and Medicaid for aging Americans.

> *It's imperative that we all get actively involved in this conversation.*

Instead, some healthcare reform advocates have spoken of funding a general health insurance program by shifting hundreds of billions of dollars *away from* Medicare and Medicaid. Not only would such a shift result in no net savings to taxpayers – it's just a shift – but it would destroy both Medicare and Medicaid.

Then what?

Again, when you run out of money, you have two choices: You can go get some more, or you can cut back on expenses. In healthcare terms, you can tax or you can ration.

These topics are too important to leave to somebody else, however noble and talented those people may be. We all need to get actively involved in a national conversation on these choices.

Part II: The Perfect Storm

Three Trends Are Threatening the Very Existence of Medicare and Medicaid

Chapter 4

Trend I – Growing Demand for Long-Term Healthcare

It's a certainty that aging Americans' health care needs are going to keep increasing. Those needs are about to cripple Medicare and Medicaid. The more stressed these programs become, the more taxation and healthcare rationing we're going to encounter.

The Alzheimer's Association predicts that by 2010 there will be 500,000 new cases of Alzheimer's disease per year, and that by 2050 there will be a million new cases each year. The likelihood of Alzheimer's doubles every five years after age 65.[1] That means more and more Alzheimer's patients in the future as people live longer. This is a particularly difficult situation because it's patients with Alzheimer's and similar long-term degenerative diseases who are most likely to need long-term care.

Why the Need is Growing

The overall U.S. population is growing but the Senior segments are growing faster. In addition, shifting patterns of immigration, legal and illegal, are changing the complexion of the country, aided and abetted by higher birthrates for (poorer) minorities than for (wealthier) majorities. To cap it off, dramatic advances in medicine and medical technology mean that Americans are living longer than ever before. Let's look at each of these more closely.

U.S. Population Increasing

The U.S. population passed the 300 million mark on October 17, 2006. From 2000 to 2008 it increased from 281 million to 304 million, or around 8% total over those eight years. The White increase was slower, 6.4% over the whole time period. All the other racial groups grew faster: Blacks, 9.4%; American Indians, 15.8%; Native Hawaiians and Pacific Islanders, 21.5%; Asians, 28%; Hispanics, over 30%.[2]

Senior Population Increasing Faster Still

From 1950 to the present, the general American population grew at about 1.2% per year. The Senior population, ages 65-74, grew at about 1.5% a year, about 25% faster. And the very Senior population (75 and over) grew at a rate nearly double that.[3]

By 2050, more than 2% of the U.S. population will be over 90. Imagine what would happen if a reliable cure for cancer or heart disease were discovered.

By 2050, the Census Bureau projects, more than 2% of the U.S. population will be over 90. Imagine what would happen if a reliable cure for cancer or heart disease were to be discovered. More than a half million people die every year from cancer, and heart disease claims another 600,000.[4] What would happen if these people didn't die, and the ranks of the elderly were to swell by another million people a year?

Immigration

Immigration is now more important than birthrate in changing the face of America. There's both legal immigration and illegal immigration to consider. Keep in mind that legal immigrants are every bit as eligible for Medicare and Medicaid benefits as native-born Americans. The eligibility of unauthorized immigrants is currently under debate.

Legal Immigration. Immigration patterns are changing from mainly European to mainly Mexican, Latin American, and Asian. Defined as people receiving their "Green Cards" in a given year, immigration, like everything else, has been trending upwards over the past decade (Table 4-1).

Table 4-1: How Many People Got Green Cards in Select Years

Region of Birth	2000	2004	2008
Total	841,002	957,883	1,107,126
Africa	44,534	66,422	105,915
Asia	264,413	334,540	383,608
Europe	130,996	133,181	119,138
North America	338,959	342,468	393,253
Oceania	5,105	5,985	5,263
South America	55,823	72,060	98,555
Unknown	1,172	3,227	1,394

Source: *Yearbook of Immigration Statistics* (2008), Table 3.
Notes: "Green Card" means Legal Resident Status.
"North American" immigration is 10:1 from Mexico.

The main areas-of-origin now are Asia (especially India and the People's Republic of China), Mexico, and the Caribbean.

The top ten states with the greatest percents of foreign-born residents are, from highest down[6]:

California, 26.2
New York, 20.4

New Jersey, 17.6
Hawaii, 17.5
Florida, 16.7
Nevada, 15.8
Texas, 13.9
District of Columbia, 12.9
Arizona, 12.8
Illinois, 12.3.

By 2060, immigrants plus their descendants will account for 105 million (63%) of the projected population increase.
Center for Immigration Studies (2007)[5]

Inflow is currently around 1.2 million a year, projected to rise to 2 million by mid-century. Census demographers used to say the U.S. population would not hit 400 million until the second half of this century. The new rate of increase is fast enough that they're now projecting we'll top that figure in 2039 and reach 439 million in 2050.

Illegal Immigration. The Pew Center tells us that there were 12 million unauthorized immigrants living in the U.S. in March 2008. The number of illegals living here has leveled off over the past decade and may actually be declining. The inflow has dropped from 800,000 a year in 2000-04 to 500,000 a year in 2005-08. But the size of the illegal population nevertheless increased from 8.4 million in 2000 to the 12 million, that is, by 40%. Illegal immigrants make up about 4% of the American population.[8]

Most illegals come from Mexico (59%) and Latin America (22%), smaller numbers from Asia (12%), Europe (4%), and Africa (4%).

Birth Rates

Birthrates have been pretty steady for the general population and for the key racial groups. The White American birthrate is on the order of 14 births per 1000 people. American Indians have about the same birth rate as Whites. But the African American birth rate is generally about two points higher than the

White American rate, and the Asian American rate is a half point higher still. Eventually – probably around 2042 -- the majority will become the minority, and vice versa.[9]

> *Immigration is now more important than birthrate in determining the complexion of America.*

Longevity Increasing

It's not just that there will be more people who will be needing long-term care. They'll also be living longer and needing care longer.

Already more Americans are living longer than ever before. It's common now to hear about parents and grandparents living into their 80s, 90s, even 100s.

The Centers for Disease Control tell us that, from 1900 through 2005:

> Life expectancy at birth increased from 46 to 75 years for men and 48 to 80 years for women.... Among men, life expectancy at age 65 rose from 12 to 17 [additional] years and among women from 12 to 20 [additional] years.[10]

That means that men who live till 65 will, on average, live to 82, women to 85. Half will live longer than those life expectancies.

Asian Americans tend to live the longest, then Latinos, then Whites, then Blacks, then Native Americans, although some of these statistical life expectancies may be shorter as a result of more deaths in early life. In all groups women enjoy longer life expectancies than men.[11]

The U.S. Department of Health and Human Services tells us that:

> In 2000, approximately 13 million Americans needed long-term care [including younger people with disabilities]. By 2050, the number is expected to increase to 27 million; the population aged 85 and older—those most at risk

for needing long-term care—is expected to increase *fivefold*.[12]

> *The first wave of the 77 million Baby Boomers is getting ready to retire.*

Increasing longevity will put massive pressure on both Medicare and Medicaid. It will also put more pressure on families for at-home care, in their efforts to avoid the higher costs of institutional care and satisfy older people's desire to stay at home as long as possible. In addition, it may lead families to hire more outside help for at-home care simply because there will be more and more elderly people relative to younger people available to care for them.

As if all that weren't enough, 77 million Baby Boomers are getting ready to retire. This is the core of the growing demand. Unless dramatic changes are made, their health care needs alone will simply overwhelm both Medicare and Medicaid.[13]

Table 4-2: For How Long Will People Need Long-term Care?

Years	Males	Females
>5	11%	28%
2-5	17%	22%
<2	29%	29%
0	42%	21%

Source: Adapted From: Kemper, P., Komisar, H. L., and Alecixh, L. (2005). Long-Term Care over an Uncertain Future: What Can Current Retirees Expect? *Inquiry, 42*(4), 335-50.

Notes: People Turning 65 in 2005.

Race and Ethnicity

Some but not all of the connection between race/ethnicity and disease may be explained by socio-economic class, e.g., crowded conditions, high-carbohydrate diets, chronic stress, and lack of exercise.

> *Men who live till 65 will – on average -- live to 82, women to 85. This means half will live even longer.*

That said, there are some connections between race and ethnicity and the kinds of illnesses that lead to especially long stays in skilled nursing facilities.[14]

Latinos and Blacks suffer disproportionately from Alzheimer's Disease. Parkinson's appears to predominate in Latinos, TB among Asians and Latinos, diabetes among Mexican Americans, Blacks, and Puerto Ricans, and high blood pressure and heart disease among Blacks, Mexican Americans, and American Indians.[15-21]

The New American Nursing Home

Table 4-2 shows how many years men and women who enter nursing homes are likely to stay there. Table 4-3 describes nursing home residents by age and race.

Table4-3: Nursing Home Residents by Age and Race

Race	All Ages	Under 65	65-74	75-84	85 and Up
White	1,276,000	127,100	134,200	405,800	608,900
Black	186,100	40,700	34,500	54,600	56,300
Other[1]	30,100	7,200	5,300	8,300	9,300
Latino	57,200	12,900	11,300	18,500	14,400

Source: National Nursing Home Survey (2004)

Notes: [1]*Other* includes Asians, Native Hawaiians and Pacific Islanders, American Indians and Alaska Natives, and a few people of multiple races.

For all the reasons we just talked about, the 21st-century American nursing home will be expected to provide skilled-nursing care for a larger number of Seniors (65-74) and especially *senior* Seniors (85-plus) than ever before. While the number of residents who simply need help with their daily activities may level off or even decrease as people seek better and less expensive care for their parents and grandparents, and eventually for themselves, those numbers will be more than made up for by increasing numbers of people with Alzheimer's, Parkinson's, ALS and other progressive, debilitating conditions, all kept alive by advances in expensive medical research, treatment, and technology. Accordingly the average stay will increase considerably, and stays of 10-20 years will become common.

Table 4-4: Major Nursing Home Resident Diagnoses

Diagnosis	People
Diabetes Mellitus	87,600
Senile Dementia	28,000
Alzheimer's Disease	145,000
Parkinson's Disease	34,700
Multiple Sclerosis	13,200

Source: National Nursing Home Survey (2004)
Notes: Approximately a fifth of Nursing Home residents have these diagnoses.
Total Nursing Home Population, 1,490,200

Moreover, the demands on staff who can deal with these debilitating conditions will increase, and an already difficult workforce problem will become even more challenging.

The Kaiser Foundation (2004) tells us that:

> Over two-thirds of long-stay residents had multiple physical conditions, and close to two-fifths had both physical and mental/cognitive conditions, up from a quarter in 1999.[22]

In other words, we are marching steadily toward the "80/20 Rule," where a small portion of the recipients receive a large portion of the benefits. Twenty-first century nursing homes will be housing the sickest of the sick – those most likely to depend on Medicaid – and housing them for longer periods of time.

The nursing home of the future will house many more very long term residents with debilitating diseases like Alzheimer's, Parkinson's, and diabetes.

Medicaid already pays less than 100% of the actual cost of nursing-home care. If these payment levels continue or worsen, and if further cutbacks are applied, more and more nursing homes will go bankrupt over the next decade, exacerbating the problems for those that stay open.[23]

Whites will still be the overwhelming majority of residents, but there will be disproportionately higher numbers of Black residents, Latino residents, and Asian residents than previously, capped only by these cultures' greater inclinations to take care of their elderly at home. Widowed and otherwise single women will make up the majority of the Senior-Senior population.

People will continue to look to Medicaid as the principal payment source, and private resources will come into play less and less as costs increase beyond the reach of all but the wealthiest families. Most long-term nursing-home residents will see their estates consumed by health-care costs, right down to their state's Medicaid impoverishment levels. For many families, inheritance will become a thing of the past.

The increasing American divorce rate and the growing inclination of people to live the single life are likely to increase the numbers of residents, if for no other reason than single people don't have spouses to take care of them at home.

The situation is similar for the growing number of people, straight and gay, who live together without benefit of marriage. In addition, unmarried people are not legally responsible for each other's care in the same way married people are.

> *The 21st-century nursing home will house people most likely to depend on Medicaid, and house them for longer periods of time.*

Nearly half of American families will have a member living in a nursing home. Experts predict that 42% of the US population aged 70 years and older will spend some time in a nursing home before they die. The US Census Bureau projects that the number of Americans 85 and older will be approximately 19 million by 2050, representing about 5% of the U.S. population.[24]

In short, the demands on the American long-term health care system will continue to increase as it deals not only with a larger number of residents but also with increasingly challenged residents. These demands will soon reach a level that neither Medicare nor Medicaid as we know them will survive. It's clear that the only way out will be to tax or to ration.

Chapter 5

Trend II – Increasing Difficulty Finding Caregivers

Recruiting and retaining quality front-line caregivers is among the least frequently mentioned problems in long-term healthcare, and one of the most intractable. A frequently proposed solution is to increase wages and benefits dramatically. Increasing compensation, however, would further accelerate Medicare's and Medicaid's collapse.

The irony is, as the number of people who need long-term care is *in*creasing, the number of people ready, willing, and able to provide that care is *de*creasing!

> *As the need for caregivers is increasing, the available workforce is decreasing.*

It's not so much the physicians. There really aren't that many physicians involved in nursing homes, and those that are involved usually maintain their own practices and stop by only when they need to see a patient. It's not even so much the nurses, even though Registered Nurses have to be on-call 24/7 in assisted-living centers and on-site around the clock in skilled nursing facilities.

The real problem is recruiting and retaining the DCW's, the direct care workers – nurses' aides, orderlies, and CNA's [Certified Nursing Assistants] -- who, for not much above minimum wage, do the stressful, demanding, and sometimes even nasty and dangerous hands-on work that comprises 70% to 80% of nursing-home care.

An article in the 2008 *Gerontologist* says that, by 2012, the number of nursing aide, orderly, and attendant jobs in nursing homes will increase by 24%.[2]

The Institute for the Future of Aging Services (IFAS) predicts that in the next few years the industry will need 800,000 new workers. Other experts predict that, by 2050, we will need *four million* more long-term care workers.[1]

And don't forget the home health aides. The same *Gerontologist* article says the need for home health aides will increase by 48%.

Keisha's Story

Keisha, now 32, was only a child herself when she had her first baby. From that moment on, motherhood controlled her life. She dropped out of high school because she needed money and the father was nowhere to be seen. With a teenager and a kindergartner at home now, her dreams of junior college were pretty well dashed. Her work as a nurses' aide was physically and emotionally draining and paid barely over minimum wage, but at least it let her be home when the boys weren't in school. She fought depression on a daily basis. She tried to follow her mother's advice: Take it one day at a time.

These are not problems that we can wait decades or even years to confront. They are already upon us. A 2003 IFAS survey found that 80% of state respondents (33 states) said direct care worker shortages are "a serious problem," and a 2004 survey by the Paraprofessional Healthcare Institute reported that 75% of states surveyed said DCW recruitment and retention was a major workforce issue.[3, 4]

> *These are not problems that can wait for decades or even years. They are already upon us.*

Nor is finding long-term care providers strictly an American problem. That same issue of *The Economist* says that all the rich nations are facing the same pressures. But the United States has larger and more diverse numbers to deal with, and perhaps a greater inclination to put our old people in nursing homes.

Who Are These "Direct Care Workers"?

IFAS tells us that 90% of direct care workers are women, about half are racial or ethnic minorities, they average 36 years of age, and about half are part-time employees.[5]

The Gerontologist adds that most of these women have dependent children, and that a third of them live in families whose income is at or below 150% of the federal poverty level.[6]

How Much Do They Get Paid?

For taking care of your mother or grandmother, the average direct-care worker (DCW) gets paid about a dollar an hour more than the fry cook at the nearest fast-food restaurant.

In 2005 the median DCW compensation was $17,710 ($8.85/hour), compared to $15,500 ($7.75/hour) for fast-food workers and $14,500 ($7.25/hour) for federal minimum-wage workers. (Remember that "median" means half the workers are paid *less* than these figures.) Nursing home workers are twice as likely to be uninsured than hospital workers. Indeed, one in four DCW's lacks health insurance. At the same time DCW's are vulnerable to all kinds of injuries from back strain to contusions.[7]

Table 5-1 shows the average hourly wages for Certified Nursing Assistants, the best paid of the direct-care workers.

Table 5-1: Average Hourly Wage for Certified Nursing Assistants (CNA's)

	Less Than One Year	More Than Ten Years
All Facilities	$9.03	$11.36
Northeast	10.42	13.06
Midwest	9.22	11.55
South	7.98	9.74
West	8.73	11.42

Source: National Nursing Assistant Survey, 2004-5, Table 21. Center for Health Statistics, Department of Health and Human Services

What About Turnover?

No surprise, but turnover is terrible. Table 5-2 summarizes how satisfied direct-care workers are with the main aspects of their jobs. It's not unusual to have to replace half to all of a facility's workforce during the course of a single year. A 2002 Wisconsin study found turnover rates of 77-164% in assisted-living centers, 99-127% in nursing homes, and 25-50% in home health agencies.[8] A 2002 North Carolina study found pretty much the same thing: 95% turnover for aides in nursing homes, and 37% in home health agencies.[9] The ACHA study of nurses' aides found a 76% turnover.[10]

> *For taking care of your mother or grandmother, the average DCW gets paid about a dollar an hour more than the fry cook at the nearest fast-food restaurant.*

Regarding CNAs, the highest-level of DCW:

> CNAs have little or no status in the healthcare community, get little or no respect, and make near poverty wages. In addition, CNAs have very little input into decision-making, scheduling, workload, or policy. They are terribly over-worked and shoulder an impossible burden on a daily basis.[11]

The work also affects DCWs' mental and emotional well-being.[12]

One final thing: Seventy percent of direct care workers report having heard patients, visitors, or staff make racist comments:

> Racism from staff was a significant predictor of job [dis] satisfaction but racism from residents was not, even though 70% of the DCWs in the sample had heard residents and clients make racist remarks. Apparently the DCWs felt the patients were too impaired really to mean what they said, but staff and visitors weren't.[13]

Table 5-2: How Satisfied with their Jobs are Direct Care Workers?

	Extremely Satisfied	Somewhat Satisfied	Somewhat Dissatisfied	Extremely Dissatisfied
Morale	26.8	51.9	12.7	7.6
Challenge	43.8	49.2	4.5	---
Benefits	22.9	40.8	14.3	19.5
Salary	18.4	41.7	18.7	20.8
New Skills	44.4	43.1	8.4	3.7

Source: National Nursing Home Survey (2004)

Note: Respondents were CNAs, the highest level of Direct Care Worker

-- Too few cases for a reliable estimate.

Who Else Could Provide Care?

The Patients' Families

Something on the order of 34 million people in this country are informal caregivers. They are mainly middle-aged, female, and between 45-64. Adult daughters provide 29% of at-home care, daughters-in-law 23%. Some sources say that two-thirds of the care-givers are women; others say as high as 85%.[14]

While caregiver-relatives report considerable satisfaction with their work, they still pay a high emotional price because of their close emotional connection with the patient.

Emotional pressures combined with economic pressures are leading families to seek more formal, institutional help. We've already noted that patients 85 and older are the fastest-growing population segment in need of long-term healthcare. If the patients are 85+, their adult children are probably in their 55-65s, often too old themselves to provide much care. Their grand-daughters (and grand-daughters-in-law) are probably 30-45 and busy building their own families and careers. Indeed, in 2008 nearly 60% of women of both generations were already employed full time.[15]

Other factors which operate against assuming that family members will be able to provide the lion's share of long-term care are birthrate and survival. Because of low birthrates, there will be fewer and fewer family members available to care for their elderly. The ratio of available family members to patients is predicted to decline from 11:1 in 1990 to 4:1 in 2050. In addition, two-thirds of nursing home residents have no living relatives.[16]

The bottom line is that informal care from family members is becoming less and less available. There's no reason to expect that this pattern will change, and many reasons to expect that it won't.

Older Americans

Wal-Mart and McDonald's have discovered that older Americans constitute a dependable and skillful workforce. Could these Senior citizens help care for citizens more Senior than themselves?

Informal care from family members is becoming less available just as the need is growing.

The Gerontologist surveyed low-income, older workers and discovered that 43% were interested in providing direct-care service – but only 28% would be willing to provide hands-on care.

In addition, the workers or the employers were concerned about transportation to and from work, unfamiliarity with the technical side of nursing-home care, and disappointment at compensation ($10+ expected, $8 offered).[17]

Combined with the fact that so much nursing home work is physically demanding, these concerns indicate that the Senior population may help but is not likely to make a big dent in the need to expand the long-term healthcare workforce.

Immigrants

Native-born Americans are unlikely to start having lots more children, so the logical direction to turn to grow the workforce is to immigrants. Immigrants have always been willing to work hard for low wages, which certainly describes jobs in the long-term healthcare industry.

In addition, people from some countries outside the U.S. are more likely to value and respect older people than many Americans are.

On the other hand, admitting larger numbers of immigrants will further swell the numbers of people eligible for Social Security, Medicare, Medicaid, and other entitlement programs, substantially exacerbating the problems we've been talking about. Language limitations may also cause problems, especially with patients who are encumbered by progressive hearing loss and cognitive impairment. And since, as we noted earlier, all the "rich" nations are facing the same kinds of problems, we may even encounter some competition for the immigrants most likely to help with the long-term healthcare problem.

Immigrants from countries that still revere their elders may provide at least a partial solution.

Nevertheless, immigrants may provide at least a partial answer to our problems.

In summary, the second force in the long-term healthcare "perfect storm" – on top of increasing numbers of people needing care and the soaring cost of providing that care – is recruiting and retaining a quality workforce. Hands-on care is a terribly difficult and financially unrewarding job, although it provides occasional emotional satisfaction. Expanding the workforce to meet the need will be among the most difficult of the long-term healthcare problems. Simple increases in compensation may help, but they would accelerate the programs' descent into bankruptcy and lead to higher taxes or more strict rationing.

Chapter 6

Trend III – The Rising Cost of Long-Term Healthcare

So, who will take care of Grandma and Grandpa once they can't take care of each other? You will. Either you'll take care of them personally or you'll pay someone to take care of them. You'll pay either through your paycheck, savings, and other assets, your federal, state, and local taxes, your lost inheritance, or, if some advocates have their way, through enforced "parent support" payments similar to child support payments for a minor – the so-called "filial responsibility" obligations that are already on the books in 30 states.[1]

> *In 30 states, your county can demand that you pay your parents' nursing-home expenses.*
>
> *National Policy Analysis Institute*

Main Approaches

The main approaches to long-term healthcare are at-home care, adult day-care, assisted-living centers, and skilled nursing facilities.[2]

At-Home Care

Nearly everybody would rather stay at home than live in some kind of institution. At-home care is not only more personal and attentive, it's cheaper, provided the patient needs help only with the six activities of daily life – eating, dressing, hygiene, toileting, maintaining continence, and moving about. More precisely, it's cheaper in monetary terms but it may be considerably more expensive in non-monetary terms, especially to the actual care-givers. We'll talk more about non-monetary costs in a later chapter.

At-home care generally involves family members and outside home-health aides, housekeepers, respite-care providers, and other allied health personnel. It offers help mainly with those activities of daily life. It keeps patients closer to the reality of day-to-day family life, with all its pleasures and pains.

Table 6-1: Average LTC Costs

Service	Median Hourly	Five-Year % Increase	
At-Home Care			
Homemaker	$17.48	2.72	
Home Health Aide	18.50	1.66	
Certified Home Aide	46.22	13.16	
Adult Day-Care	9.91	N/A	
	Monthly		
Assisted Living			
Private One BR	2,825	4.72	
	Daily		**Annual**
Nursing Home			
Semi-Private Room	183	4.71	$66.886
Private Room	203	4.27	$74,208

Source: Genworth 2009 Cost-of-Care Survey
https://pro.genworth.com/content/etc/medialib/genworth_v2/pdf/ltc_cost_of_care.Par.73347.File.dat/Summary%20of%20Findings_gnw.pdf

The primary at-home care-giver is likely to be the daughter, daughter-in-law, or other female. Although she will probably find some satisfaction in the work, she's likely to burn out quickly, probably in about a year. She may very well need help from a part- or full-time housekeeper or home health aide.

Nearly everybody would rather stay at home than live in some kind of institution.

While Medicare may pay for some "home-bound" care, it does not, as we emphasized in Chapter 2, pay for "at-home" care. Medicaid will not pay anything toward at-home care. Program authorities certainly know that at-home care costs less, but they are understandably worried about the enormous potential for fraud.

In some locations around the country, a special Medicare/Medicaid program called PACE provides support services intended to help people stay in their homes: Primary care services, social services, and other supportive services.[3]

Some long-term health care insurance policies pay for some at-home services when those services are rendered as part of a doctor-approved plan of care.

In most places there are local programs that will help support home care, like Meals-on-Wheels and respite programs.[4]

Genworth Financial provides a wonderful interactive map that shows the most recent average costs for at-home care, adult day-care facilities, assisted-living centers, and skilled nursing facilities in various parts of every state.[5] Table 6-1 shows the average price of key services. Table 6-2 shows the costs of different kinds of care in four states in various parts of the country. The costs vary dramatically, mainly as a function of geographical differences in staff salaries.

For families that hire home health aides to work along with or instead of family members, another Genworth report[6] tells us that home health-aide hourly wages have held pretty steady over recent years. Hourly at-home care increased only 1.7% this past year, to $18.50 in 2009.

The primary at-home caregiver may very well need a part- or full-time housekeeper or home health aide.

This steadiness may be the result of the current economic recession, so when the recession ends and competition for workers resumes, home health aide costs may begin to rise again.

Adult Day Care

Adult day-care centers are respite facilities that not only give at-home caregivers a break but also provide health services, therapeutic services, and social activities for people with significant physical and cognitive problems. The typical adult day-care center offers programs designed for its particular population, e.g., mental stimulation for dementia patients, along with medical services from an on-site RN.

Table 6-2: Average Statewide Healthcare Costs, Selected States

Types of Care/ Selected States	Home Health Aide	Adult Day Care	Assisted Living Center	Skilled Nursing Facility
Connecticut	$56,056	18,980	37,800	129,028
Iowa	$49,192	12,675	30,384	51,830
Georgia	$36,894	16,770	25,200	57,365
Washington	$45,760	13,000	36,000	83,892

Source: Genworth Financial Annual Care Costs in 2009 http://www.genworth.com/content/genworth/us/en/products/long_termcare/long_term_care/cost_of_care.htm.

Notes: Total-State Estimates. Assumes Full-Time Care, Private Rooms.

Charges range from $25-$75 a day, averaging a little over $50. Some facilities offer "scholarships," and others use a sliding fee scale based on income. Medicare won't pay for day-care services, but Medicaid might, depending on just what services are offered. Regular health insurance will sometimes pay, if licensed medical personnel are involved. Long-term healthcare insurance may pay too, depending on the policy. Dependent tax credits may also apply.[7]

Significant dollars could be saved if the Medicare and Medicaid authorities could find ways to support at-home healthcare arrangements.

Hourly adult day care costs in 2009 averaged $9.91/hour (no data from previous years).[8]

The National Respite Network and Resource Center provides useful information about adult day-care centers.[9] In addition, the American Health Care Association supplies a helpful "Home Care Finder" to help you think about the kind of facility you need and identify possibilities in your area.[10]

Assisted-Living Centers

Assisted-living centers are midway between living at home and living in a skilled nursing facility. Assisted-living centers are for people who need help with some of the activities of daily living but don't need 24-hour care. These facilities generally provide private rooms or apartments, central recreational facilities, and a communal dining option. Some offer a rich array of social activities on and off the grounds.

Monthly charges generally run from around $2,000 to around $4,000, depending on part of the country and quality of the facility. North Dakota ($25,049) had the least expensive assisted-living centers, Massachusetts the most expensive

($55,137).

Medicare doesn't pay for assisted living. Medicaid may cover part of the cost, if the Senior meets her state's eligibility requirements and would otherwise wind up in a more expensive skilled nursing facility.

Most long-term healthcare insurance policies also cover assisted-living facilities, and the Veterans Administration offers special benefits for wartime veterans and their spouses.[11] But the vast majority of assisted-living costs are paid by private funds.

Assisted living centers generally cost $2-4,000 a month, about half what a nursing home costs.

As nursing-home costs continue to rise, we can anticipate more people wanting to stay longer in assisted-living centers, and as assisted-living costs continue to rise, more people will want to keep living at home, particularly when adult day-care facilities are available. It's clear that significant dollars can be saved if the Medicare and Medicaid authorities could find ways to support at-home living arrangements. (See also "Affinity Groups," Chapter 14, below.)

Some assisted-living facilities are wonderful places to live, providing safe, comfortable space, privacy, stimulating programs, and social opportunities. The problem is, once Grandma reaches the point that she can't really take care of herself, the assisted-living managers will ask her to move on to a skilled nursing facility. So she will have to expect to be uprooted, perhaps when she's feeling vulnerable and stability is particularly important to her.

In addition to its "Home Care Finder," the American Health Care Association also supplies a particularly helpful "Facility Finder" to help you think about assisted-living centers and nursing homes, and identify possibilities in your area.[12]

Skilled Nursing Facilities

The skilled nursing facility, what most people call a "nursing home," is a board-and-care facility staffed 24/7 for very frail people who can't stay in their homes because of physical problems, cognitive disabilities, or both.[13] It provides skilled nursing care along with intermediate nursing care and custodial care, all the levels of care an aging or disabled person is likely to need.

On the skilled level, skilled nursing facilities employ Registered Nurses who can care for wounds, administer antibiotics, and provide other advanced services under the direction of a physician. Skilled nursing facilities also have on-site or on-call a variety of other highly trained people like physical therapists, occupational therapists, and speech therapists.

On the intermediate level they provide assistance with medical conditions that require daily monitoring but not 24-hour attention. These services are generally ordered by a physician and supervised by a Registered Nurse, although nurses' aides and nursing assistants are often involved.

Skilled nursing facilities also provide custodial care, that is, room, board, and assistance with the six activities of daily life.

The average nursing-home room now costs about $6,500 a month, half that in some areas, double in others.

Many have special units for special populations, e.g., an Alzheimer's unit or a hospice.

Louisiana had the least expensive skilled nursing facilities ($45,625 for a semi-private room); Connecticut, of the 48 contiguous, had the most expensive ($117,895). In Alaska, the average semi-private room today costs $219,913 for the year. But you can see Russia from there.

Since Medicare won't help except for limited

"rehabilitative" stays, the alternatives are personal and family resources, Medicaid, and long-term care insurance (not regular health insurance).

Table 6-3 shows not only how skilled-nursing costs have been rising over the years, but how they vary across regions of the country. Table 6-4 tells how patients of various ages pay for care.

Table 6-3: Estimated Annual Private-Pay Nursing-Home Charges

	1985	1995	2005	2009
National	$17,400	36,972	74,000	78,000
Northeast	$19,740	49,404	99,000	104,000
West	$17,976	43,992	88,000	92,000
South	$16,308	35,340	71,000	74,000
Midwest	$16,776	31,800	64,000	67,000

Source: Centers for Disease Control, U.S. Department of Health and Human Services. Compiled by Elderweb.

Notes: 2005 and 2009 estimates by extrapolation. In the absence of better regional data, we increased costs each year by the over-all estimated rate of nursing-home inflation, presenting rounded numbers to discourage over-interpretation.

As to Medicaid, the individual states make the eligibility rules, under federal guidelines.[14] The rules are severe. Grandma has to use up pretty much all her assets – savings, investments, retirement plan, house, just about everything. Only then will Medicaid take over her expenses.

It used to be that, with some advance planning and a good elder-law specialist, Grandma could give some of her property away, put the rest in an irrevocable trust, and go onto Medicaid. The effect, of course, was to preserve most of her estate for her favorite heirs and charities. Congress took a dim view of these techniques, however, and banned them. It even prohibited attorneys and financial planners from *talking* about them!

Long-Term Healthcare Insurance

Long-term healthcare insurance is just about the only asset-protection tool left. Although these policies vary from company to company, they generally pay the lion's share of nursing home expenses and assisted-living expenses, even some at-home care expenses.

Table 6-4: How Do Nursing Home Residents Pay for Care?

	Population	Personal	Medicare	Medicaid	Other
All Residents	1,492,200	255,300	118,400	875,300	54,400
Under 65	174,900	10,200	7,100	119,800	10,800
65-74	174,100	16,700	14,800	110,900	7,600
75-84	468,700	72,400	44,300	267,700	17,700
85 and Up	674,500	156,000	52,200	376,900	18,300
Male	430,500	69,400	36,900	230,500	25,100
Female	1,061,700	185,900	81,400	644,800	29,300
White	1,276,000	246,800	105,100	717,400	47,100
Black	186,100	5,700	11,000	136,800	6,200
Latino	57,200	4,200	39,100	---	---

Source: National Nursing Home Survey (2004).

You can purchase individual policies privately. You might also be able to purchase a group policy through your employer or professional association.

In individual and group policies, you choose the waiting period (generally 90 days, to coordinate with the Medicare payment period), the benefit amount (e.g., $100, $150 per day), and the number of years' coverage (usually 3, 5, 10, or lifetime).

By the time most people start thinking about long-term healthcare insurance, though, premiums are pretty steep, so you have to evaluate the cost/benefit carefully. Moreover, if you've started to show signs of Alzheimer's, Parkinson's, diabetes, or other serious conditions, you may not be able to buy long-term care insurance.

In many states you can now buy a special kind of long-term healthcare insurance designed to protect a portion of Grandma's assets.

Because you purchase long-term care insurance years, even decades, before you're likely to need it, every policy should have an inflation adjustment that will hopefully match the rising costs of care.

A little better than half of nursing home residents stay for longer than four years. As medical science and technology extend life, the stays are growing longer still. Accordingly, even though it costs more, a life-time benefits policy makes a lot of sense. Not all companies offer life-time benefits, however, and with those that do, the premium may be prohibitively high.

Even for the best actuaries, pricing long-term care insurance is a tricky business. On the one hand, you want to price it low enough so people will buy it. On the other, you want to have enough premium income coming in so the company stays solvent. One of the biggest problems is "adverse selection," which means that the people who are most likely to buy the insurance are the people most likely to use it.

The bottom line is that LTC policies are expensive, particularly if you wait to buy them until you're in your sixties. But they should probably be even *more* expensive. At current premium rates, it's doubtful that companies will be able to pay all the benefits they've agreed to cover. Indeed, many companies have stopped writing LTC policies, and some have isolated their LTC business in separate corporations so they can declare bankruptcy if claims become too demanding.

Soon the only game in town may be some form of government-run basic LTC insurance.

Some financial planners suggest that you use the same premium to purchase cash-value life insurance instead. Their argument is that there are one or two chances out of four that you'll end up in a nursing home for more than a short period of time, but four chances out of four that you'll die some day. LTC insurance *might* pay off; life insurance *will* pay off.

In some states – California, Connecticut, Indiana, Minnesota, and New York, with more joining the list every year – a program called Partnerships for Long-Term Care lets consumers buy a special kind of long-term care policy designed to protect a portion Grandma's assets. The individual states make the rules, some more restrictive than others. Generally you can protect one dollar of assets for every dollar you spend on long-term healthcare.[15]

These policies cost about the same as regular LTC policies.

Additional Kinds of Facilities

In addition to the main four just described, there are a variety of other approaches to long-term care. It's reasonable to anticipate that additional variations will appear as managers seek the most cost/effective arrangements for the largest numbers of similar patients, emphasizing the less expensive and more homelike.

Board and Care Homes

Board-and-care homes are similar to assisted-living centers but generally smaller and more limited in the services they provide. Some states require licensing, others do not. Especially at the lower end of the scale, board and care homes may be significantly cheaper than assisted-living centers.

Board-and-care centers cannot provide any form of nursing care and are therefore ineligible for Medicare or Medicaid payment.

People with very low incomes may use Supplementary Social Security benefits to pay for board-and-care living.

Independent Living Facilities

Independent-living facilities offer full-fledged individual apartments in a community setting, along with a communal-dining option. Private-pay rents range from $1,500 up. Some Independent Living Facilities are subsidized by HUD, the US Department of Housing and Urban Development. HUD-subsidized rents may start below $500/month. Subsidized apartments often involve long waiting lists.

Palliative Care and Hospice Care Centers

Palliative Care Centers specialize in controlling pain and providing comfort at any stage in an illness. Hospice care centers specialize in helping people achieve a peaceful and dignified death. Hospice care always includes palliative care but palliative care does not necessarily include hospice care.

Palliative and hospice care services are delivered by specially trained doctors, nurses, and other therapists in hospitals, skilled nursing facilities, even at home.

Many regular health insurance policies cover palliative and hospice care. So, within limits, do Medicare and Medicaid.

Continuing-Care Retirement Communities

A continuing-care retirement community (CCRC) is a facility that offers a number of options from independent apartments or even stand-alone houses to skilled nursing facilities and even hospice services. Residents generally start at the independent end of the spectrum and progress to the hospice level.

Entry into a Continuing Care Retirement Community often requires a fee that is prohibitive for many people. Most people who can pay the fee pay it from private sources, many selling their homes to free up the money. In some cases, the facility guarantees lifetime care services in exchange for the admission fee, but there have been some instances in which the management underestimated the future cost of providing benefits and as a result filed for bankruptcy.

To summarize, the cost of long-term healthcare is so high that, if Medicaid fails, only the wealthiest Americans will be able to pay for skilled-nursing care. While there will almost surely be incentives to take care of Grandma at home, the government will somehow have to provide residential and skilled-nursing support for our impoverished frail elderly. So we'll all be caught between finding the best care we can afford for our own family members and coping with inevitable increases in taxation and rationing caused by the public long-term care safety net. Soon the only game in town will be some form of mandated basic long-term care insurance (the Kennedy plan), supplemented by private long-term care policies for those who can afford them.

Chapter 7

Consequences of Rising Long-Term Care Costs

Rising healthcare costs affect not only the abstract notion of "economy," they impact *people*. Indeed they mainly affect some of the most vulnerable people in our society, the frail elderly, and their families.

> *Rising healthcare costs affect not only the abstract notion of "economy," they impact people.*

Rising costs affect people directly and indirectly. Directly, as we'll see in a moment, they cause anxiety and worse. Indirectly they may cause society in general to re-think its positions on important healthcare topics, and to effect changes which in turn impact the same vulnerable people.

Direct Effects on the Frail Elderly

Anxiety

Rising healthcare costs add to the natural anxiety that many elderly people experience. Worry over where the money's going to come from to pay her living expenses, worry about what the family's giving up, worry about becoming a burden on her children and grandchildren – these are the key anxieties that weigh on Grandma's mind.

Feelings of Loss

Old age is, in many respects, a period of loss. Not just the loss of physical faculties but the psychological loss the physical losses trigger:[1]

> Lost control triggers *fear for one's safety and security.*
> Lost companionship triggers *fear of abandonment.*
> Lost faculties trigger *fear of incompetence.*
> Lost mobility triggers *fear of confinement.*

Elder Abuse

Although statistics on this topic are hard to come by, field reports say that elder abuse[2] is on the rise.[3] As stress builds, some family members take their frustrations out on their elderly parents or grandparents – emotionally, through harsh and recriminating words; physically, through a pinch, a slap, a shove, or worse. As offspring watch money that would otherwise have gone to them go instead to the nursing home, some of them, too, will take out their frustrations on elderly patients. In addition to physical abuse, financial abuse seems to be an ever-increasing issue.

Despair and Suicide

On the heels of all this loss can come frustration, depression, even despair. Someday, maybe when she discovers that the money that's keeping her in the nursing home is her grandson's college fund, Grandma may simply reach for the pill bottle.

Elder abuse and suicide are on the rise.

Despite the lingering taboo on the subject, it's important to recognize that surprising numbers of middle-aged people say privately that they'd rather take their own lives than have to endure what they see aged relatives and friends experiencing. It's hard to know whether they'll still feel this way when they approach nursing-home age, and it's hard to know if, when they reach nursing-home age, they will have the ways and means to carry out the deed. But there's something happening in our culture that's making it easier at least to talk about suicide. Indeed, we personally know any number of late middle-aged people who are stockpiling pills for just this eventuality.

This is an entirely separate question from "voluntary euthanasia," or physician-assisted suicide, which we will discuss later.

Direct Effects on Families

Workload

As we've said, taking care of Grandma is going to affect everybody in the family.

Mom for sure. She'll probably carry most of the burden.

Dad too. He may not make as many visits to the nursing home as Mom does or be as involved in the daily details of at-home care, but he'll feel Mom's absence and he'll have to help out with tasks that she'd normally take care of all by herself. He'll also have to spell her from time to time – "respite care" – and deal with the periodic tension and conflict that come from changing roles, growing workloads, re-arranged lives, and just plain fatigue.

Either Mom or Dad might even feel a little guilty about having put Grandma in a nursing home, or not visiting her more often.

Bear in mind that Grandma may be in her 80s or 90s, which means that Mom may be in her 60s or 70s and not the indefatigable woman she was when she was younger. She may not have young kids to take care of any more or a job to attend to every day; but she may not have her full measure of youthful energy either. Indeed, one observer remarked recently that the main reason very elderly nursing home patients didn't get a lot of visitors is that their adult children were too feeble to travel. If Mom is in her 40s or 50s, either because Grandma and Grandpa decided to have kids late or because they needed long-term care relatively early, she and Dad may have an entirely different set of responsibilities: Preparing for their own retirement, for example versus helping get their own kids through college or graduate school or otherwise launched into adult life.

The older Grandma's children are, the more likely it will be that the grandchildren, especially the granddaughters, will become the "Sandwich Generation," simultaneously caring for Grandma and their own children. In other parts of the world, this shift to the upcoming generation would be quite natural. Whether American culture with its geographical fluidity, its focus on career-building, and its emphasis on the independence of the nuclear family, is ready for that shift is up for debate. It's probably not.

> *The grandchildren, especially granddaughters, will become the next "Sandwich Generation."*

Doing Without

As expenses mount up and assets vanish, everybody – Grandma and Grandpa, Mom and Dad, their siblings, maybe even the grandchildren – may all have to deal with more limited budgets. What they will have to do without will depend on the wealth level and values of the family.

Profoundly poor families won't be affected, because they have no discretionary assets and because Medicaid (or some new governmental program) will provide for their elderly members.

Working class families who previously could afford little luxuries – a vacation, a fishing boat, a nice prom dress – may not be able to enjoy those kinds of things any more. In terms of discretionary income, they will be reduced to the level of the lower classes.

Immensely wealthy families won't be affected much either, even though they'd rather be doing something else with the money that's going to the nursing homes.

As usual, it's middle-class families that will experience the greatest effect, because what they'll lose may be all they've got. Especially if Grandma's got a long-term disease or disability, middle-class families may not only lose any bequests they might have otherwise enjoyed, but, if filial responsibility laws kick in, they may have to come up with some money to handle Grandma's monthly shortfalls.

Foregone Bequests and Gifts

A special consequence of losing everything you've got is that you can't make bequests or gifts any more.[4]

Bequests and gifts are more than money and property. They are bits and pieces of ourselves. Just like the rest of Grandma's and Grandpa's assets, gifts communicate safety and security, affection and belonging, competence and success, and individuality and freedom. One of the cruelest things about long-term health care expenses is that they prevent Grandma and Grandpa from communicating these messages fully to the next generations, and prevent the children and grand-children from receiving those messages.

Resentment and Hostility

When resources are threatened, people get scared, and they respond to the threat in their own peculiar ways. Some become more aggressive. Some become hostile. Some hide out. Some try to cheat, even other family members. The seamy underside of families, usually well hidden, is most likely to show itself when there's prolonged stress

Indirect Effects through the Nursing Home

Change in Nursing Home Clientele

If you visit a Skilled Nursing Facility, you'll encounter a wide range of patients. Some will be up and around, talking with visitors, reading magazines, or participating in scheduled activities. Others will be sitting in the common areas, maybe watching TV, maybe just staring at the set. Many will be in wheel chairs, some in special chairs that they're less likely to slide out of. Still others will be in their rooms, in a recliner or even in bed. And some you probably won't see, especially people with advanced dementia, because they'll be in security units that prevent them from wandering away.

As costs increase, you'll be likely to encounter a higher proportion of the more difficult cases, physical and cognitive.

As financial pressures rise, people will stay at home or in assisted-living centers for as long as they possibly can. You'll also see as many patients as possible who'd normally be in hospitals now discharged to nursing homes. Even ten years ago it would have been rare for a patient on IVs to be transferred to a nursing home; now it's commonplace. You'll see the same thing with patients suffering difficult wounds, post-surgical patients, and patients on complex medication regimes.

You'll see the same pattern in assisted-living centers, an increase in the more demanding patients and a decrease in patients who are easier to handle. Patients who could possibly stay at home will stay at home. Patients who a few years ago would have transferred into a skilled nursing facility will stay in the assisted-living center.

Nursing homes will be increasingly for the sickest of the sick.

The sickest of the sick will be in skilled nursing facilities, multiplying the cost of care, compounding the demands on staff, and depressing the social atmosphere of the facility. Patients may have to travel farther to find an appropriate level of care, and they may be transferred more often, suffering "transfer trauma" as they are forced to adjust to new surroundings.

As one seasoned nursing-home administrator remarked, "If I had known twenty years ago how tough this job would turn out to be, I'd never have gone into the business."

Indirect Effects from Societal Frustration

As the number of frail elderly needing long-term care grows – Think Alzheimer's patients, and advances in medicine and medical technology; think Baby Boomers – and society sees more clearly what sacrifices have to be made to continue taking care of old people, there will be complaints about how long-term care is adversely affecting other social needs. There will be movements to shift increasing amounts of money to other programs. Indeed, the beginnings of such movements are already clear.

There will be demands that the government apply increasingly strict forms of rationing, including deprivation of some life-saving procedures and medications.

There may even be calls for less-than-fully voluntary euthanasia.

To summarize, the message of this chapter is that soaring healthcare costs don't affect just some abstract notion of "economy," they affect *people*, mainly the frail, elderly people who inhabit our nursing homes, and their families. The effects center in anxiety and depression, and the results range from worry to suicide on the patient level, and from increased workload to frustration and aggression on the family level. As time goes on and the pressures worsen, society in general may begin to re-think its attitudes toward long-term healthcare for aging Americans. It's reasonable to expect demands for stricter rationing, even calls for involuntary euthanasia.

Chapter 8

Why Does Long-Term Healthcare Cost So Much?

People who write about why long-term healthcare costs so much all seem to have their favorite targets. It's the insurance companies. No, it's the drug companies. No, it's how much doctors get paid. No, it's over-zealous government regulators. No, it's over-caring for the sickest of the sick who are going to die soon anyway.

The fact of the matter is that there are many individuals and organizations that have their fingers in the healthcare pie, and nearly every one of them has found a way to make a lot of money. No surprise that so many people don't want things to change.

Many individuals and organizations that have their fingers in the healthcare pie have found a way to make a lot of money.

Let's look first at monetary costs – plain old cash money – and then non-monetary costs, like stress and anxiety.

Monetary Costs

These things all work together to strain your healthcare dollar:

Advances in Technology

Walk into a Best Buy today, and try to remember what it was like ten or twenty years ago. There's no comparison. The technological advances are amazing. It's the same in medicine. And every advance costs money that has to be recouped somehow, some time.

Moreover, the more technology there is, the greater the tendency to use it -- because it's good medical practice, it's interesting, it's profitable, and because it's good protection against possible malpractice claims.

Patients with Multiple Diagnoses

As though it's not enough that the number of aging people is increasing, more than a third of Medicare recipients are suffering three or more serious maladies.[1] Twenty percent of the patients require eighty percent of the care. Not just the count but the interaction among these sicknesses and disabilities drives medicine and treatment costs up. Moreover, as modern medicine solves more and more of people's health problems, the problems that are left will be the really complex and difficult ones.

Liability Insurance for Physicians and Facilities

We all know that there are patients who will sue a doctor or facility at the drop of a hat, and lawyers that will be happy to turn any slip into a federal case. So liability insurance premiums are a major influence on health care costs, especially in some specialties.

Defensive Medicine

Related to liability insurance is an understandable inclination on the part of doctors and facilities to practice "cover-your-backside" medicine. More tests equals a better defense if somebody sues you, even though excessive testing increases overall healthcare costs considerably.

Insurance Company Administration

Some experts say that competition from a government-operated or perhaps "cooperative" health insurance companies would force private insurance companies to become more efficient and lower their administrative charges. Other experts just smile and say "Post Office."

Cuts in Outside Funding

Especially when the economy is in recession, foundation and government programs to help with long-term health care costs dry up. It's the same with individual philanthropy – when it's most needed, it's least available.

Competition for Patients

Like all businesses, hospitals, assisted-living centers, and nursing homes compete for patients. What attract valuable private-pay patients are programs with a personal touch – lots of staff with the time and interest to pay attention to Grandma and Grandpa.

Staffing, of course, is the most expensive part of running a health-care facility, so even minor competitive improvements cost a lot of money.[2] Beyond that, the government tightly regulates the staffing ratios it will reimburse for nursing home care.

Drug and Related Mark-ups

Everybody knows that drug manufacturers need to recoup their research costs. What people aren't so sure of is whether their approach is fair. After all, Americans pay a lot more for the same drug than people in other countries do, including Canada. In addition, people have noticed that the drug companies spend a lot more on marketing than on research. Working with the Obama administration and AARP, drug companies have recently agreed to pricing changes that should benefit many older Americans. It remains to be seen how this will shake out. With regard to non-prescription drugs and related products, every so often you read a newspaper story about an $8 aspirin tablet or a $20 box of Kleenex. We've also seem amazing charges for packaging and delivering basic over-the-counter medications to a nursing home. What we haven't seen is a good explanation for these charges.

Failure to Monitor Costs

Some doctors, hospitals, assisted-living centers, and nursing homes – and patients! -- forget that it's somebody else's money, often the taxpayers', that's paying for the goods and services they're using. Some doctors prescribe medications that cost $2,000 per dose when a perfectly suitable alternative is available at one-tenth the cost. Some prescribe the high-dollar drug when insurance is paying for it, the cheaper alternative when it's private pay. A hospital might charge double for the same procedure than another hospital in the same locality might charge, and higher still when there's an insurance company involved.

Failure to Practice Evidence-Based Medicine

The Mayo Clinic, the Cleveland Clinic, and other highly respected clinics and hospitals are successfully reducing cost and improving care by practicing "evidence-based" medicine. Procedures and medications their physicians recommend must (whenever possible) be supported by empirical evidence of effectiveness.[3] Note the conceptual similarity between doctors using only proven treatments and medications and rationing.

The Mayo Clinic, the Cleveland Clinic, and other highly respected clinics and hospitals are successfully reducing cost and improving care by practicing "evidence-based" medicine.

Physician Compensation

Of course doctors ought to be well paid. Think of the expensive training, the loans, the costs of operating a practice, the liability insurance, the intensity and importance of the work. It's like with drug companies – Nobody doubts the justice of paying well for their services. But there are two questions in this regard: First, How well paid is "well paid"? Second, does the nature of the compensation encourage or discourage quality practice?

> *The two major causes of high healthcare costs are over-utilization by physicians practicing defensive medicine and a relatively new entrepreneurial spirit among doctors.*
> New Yorker (2009)

Physicians Entrepreneurship

The dirty little secret in medicine – one that bothers dedicated doctors as much as it bothers lay people – is that some doctor-investors buy treatment facilities, even entire specialty hospitals, and high write-off technology like CT scanners, and then they and their friends *over-refer* patients to those facilities. Conflicts of interest like this violate the code of medical ethics, but that doesn't mean they don't happen every day.

Meeting Government Regulations

The regulations handbook for nursing homes is inches thick. Studying and implementing these regulations is a dizzying task, and a major expense, for every long-term healthcare facility.

Over-Utilization by Physicians

A fascinating 2009 article by a surgeon/writer in the *New Yorker* concluded that the two major causes of high healthcare costs are over-utilization by physicians practicing defensive medicine, and a relatively new entrepreneurial spirit among many doctors that leads them to take advantage of every opportunity to make more money.

Over-Utilization by Patients

Increasing numbers of Americans of all ages are seeking the perfect life through prescription drugs. Especially popular drugs are Cymbalta, Xanax, and Zoloft for anxiety, Paxil and Prozac for depression, and, of course, Viagra, Cialis, and Levitra for erectile dysfunction. In the same vein, patients seem to be responding enthusiastically to direct-to-consumer drug ads and the ubiquitous ads for "free" scooters, diabetes supplies, and other items Medicare and Medicaid pay for.

End-of-Life Treatment Costs

The Robert Wood Johnson Foundation reports that fully 25% of Medicare's annual healthcare budget goes to expenses incurred during the last twelve months of life and that the average nursing-home patient incurs $40,000 in final-year expenses over and above residential expenses. Moreover, many individuals will be disabled with their final fatal disease for an average of three years before death. Increasing numbers of observers are questioning whether these expenditures are appropriate, given that the patient is likely to die soon anyway.[4]

> *The average nursing-home patient incurs $40,000 in final-year expenses over and above residential expenses.*
> *Robert Wood Johnson Foundation (2003)*

Fraud and Inefficiency

There's nothing more infuriating in healthcare than the amount of fraud against Medicare and Medicaid. Experts estimate that something like 30 *billion* taxpayer dollars are stolen from the two programs every year. At $75,000 per nursing-home patient per year, just think how many patients could be served by that money, even if only a quarter of it could be recovered! Until recently, neither the federal government nor the vast majority of states have done much more than talk about the problem.[5]

There's no reason to expect that things will be much better under whatever new programs Congress and the Administration come up with. In fact, the bad guys will probably find new and even more profitable ways to scam the systems. On the other hand, there have been encouraging successes at identifying and arresting malefactors recently, coincident with the Congressional healthcare debate.

Nevertheless, it's hard not to be skeptical about proposals that will fund healthcare by eliminating fraud and inefficiency.

Non-Monetary Costs

Lots of people talk about the monetary costs of long-term health care. Very few talk about the non-monetary costs, like what happens if Mom has to quit her job to take care of Grandma at home. Non-monetary costs can apply to any kind of long-term care but they apply especially to at-home care.

For better or for worse, as we noted in the preceding chapter, the reality in our culture is that it's Mom or some other female family member who generally carries the ball in taking care of her parents, grandparents, older siblings or her aging in-laws. For better or for worse, Dad typically worries more about the money -- or is deceased or in poor health himself -- and Mom worries more about the time burden.

Regardless of who takes on the time burden, these are the main non-monetary costs:

Career Costs. Lost seniority and the job-security and promotion possibilities that disappear with it; Lost career satisfaction; Lost opportunity to contribute to society.

Social Costs. Lost opportunity to participate in family life; Lost contact with friends and neighbors.

Stress and Anxiety. Worry about protecting and distributing Grandma's assets; Worry about paying Grandma's bills, as well as her own; Worry about overlooking family members' needs.

Special circumstances bring special kinds of stress, as when Grandma takes a turn for the worse, or your goofy sibling decides to try to take control.

And what if there's another Grandma who needs care, his and hers? And maybe a Grandpa too?

In summary, why long-term healthcare costs so much is a terribly complicated question. High monetary costs are the result of a complex interplay of the many elements we touched on here, along with subtle but very powerful cultural forces: A growing entrepreneurial spirit on part of many providers that has changed healthcare from a human service to a business opportunity, and a worsening "moral hazard" on the part of many consumers that leads them to insist on healthcare services and products without regard to cost. These forces combine with the growing numbers of people who need long-term care to create the dilemma we now have to resolve.

Chapter 9

Second Recapitulation

How did we get into this position? Like the fabled Perfect Storm, three forces have been combining to threaten Medicare's and Medicaid's very existence. We see no reason to expect that any of these will ease up in the foreseeable future.

Growing Demand for Services

Population increases, legal and illegal immigration, and increasing longevity are increasing the demand for long-term healthcare. While the average stay in a nursing home is a little over four years, patients suffering from long-term debilitating diseases like Alzheimer's, Parkinson's, and diabetes can be expect to need nursing-home care for five, ten, even twenty years. Keep in mind that the first wave of the 77 million Baby Boomers is about to retire, and it will be only a matter of time until half of them – 38.5 million! -- will need nursing-home care. All the possible solutions will be controversial but we need to put them all on the table if we're going to have a constructive conversation: *Limit immigration,* which has become more important than birthrate in determining population growth; *Repeal those Nanny Laws* that inhibit personal responsibility and worsen the demand on long-term care; *Permit totally voluntary physician-assisted suicide.*

Increasing Difficulty Finding and Keeping Front-Line Staff

The physical and emotional demands of direct-care work in nursing homes combined with long hours and low pay is making it increasingly difficult to recruit and retain good front-line staff. For solution one first thinks of dramatic pay hikes, but that would only worsen the financial problems. Indeed, it's hard to think of solutions to this problem, but changes in immigration laws to favor immigrants who come from countries that revere the elderly and who would be willing to work as direct-care workers for a specified period of time looks promising. The Affinity Groups program we will discuss in Chapter 14 below could also be very helpful, as could an expansion of the Americorps elder-care program.

Soaring Costs of Care

Healthcare costs are rising far faster than incomes, physician and hospital charges at nearly triple the rate of inflation, prescription drug charges at quadruple that. The nursing home of the future will be for the sickest of the sick, and the costs of treating those people will rise accordingly. As costs rise one can expect increasing numbers of physicians and allied health workers to leave the field in search of more satisfying and rewarding careers, and more nursing homes to fall into bankruptcy. While the frequently proposed efforts to reduce cost would help – reduce inefficiency, eliminate fraud, control the insurance companies, and so forth – the truly effective ways to control costs are repugnant to most Americans: Increase taxes and ration healthcare. Nevertheless, any truly effective "healthcare reform" will center in one or the other of those remedies – most likely, both.

The soaring costs of healthcare don't just affect some abstract notion of "economy." They affect *people*, mainly frail, elderly women and their families – your mother, your grandmother, your older siblings, your aging in-laws.

The greater the financial pressures, the more worry patients and their families have to deal with, and the deeper the sense of loss, the greater the risk of elder abuse – physical, emotional, financial -- and the greater the incidence of depression and suicide. Already white males over 65 are the group most likely to take their own lives.

Is at-home care an option? When families try to provide basic care for their elderly at home, the monetary costs may go down but the non-monetary costs skyrocket: Stress and strain, lost career opportunities for the principal caregiver (usually a daughter or grand-daughter), and a general disruption of the family routine.

If the at-home care must include more than the six activities of daily life -- eating, dressing, hygiene, toileting, continence, and moving about – the costs, all told, will often be competitive with the costs of institutional care.

Controlling healthcare costs will surely require some difficult changes in the culture of healthcare.

The people soaring costs affect are not just the patients and their families. Staff and administrators will feel more stress as budgets become even tighter, and other patients may begin to feel neglected. Decision-makers will feel frustrated when they have to cut back or shut down good programs because there isn't enough money to do everything that should be done. Everyone who has any connection with long-term healthcare will feel the burden.

Why healthcare costs so much is an enormously complicated question. Everyone who writes about it seems to have a favorite target: Insurance companies, drug companies, doctors, lawyers, over-zealous government regulators, crooks.... The fact of the matter is that high healthcare costs are the result of a combination of many factors, not the least of which are cultural changes that have influenced how providers and patients view contemporary healthcare.

Controlling healthcare costs will surely require some difficult changes in the culture of healthcare. The increasingly entrepreneurial spirit of contemporary healthcare, the voracious appetites of medical malpractice lawyers that force doctors to practice defensive medicine, and the insistence on the part of patients to get every treatment they can think of "right here, right now" – all these and more need to change if we are to have any hope to controlling healthcare costs in the future.

Part III: Healthcare Rationing:

It's Here, and It's Expanding

Chapter 10

Empirical Rationing

Rationing is as much or more a part of the long-term care debate as of the general healthcare debate. Long-term care for aging Americans depends on Medicare and Medicaid, and rationing is already occurring in both those programs on a daily basis, with much more in the offing. Moreover, when advocates of some of the general healthcare proposals talk about transferring billions of dollars from Medicare and Medicaid to a new national health insurance program, the implication is strong that the lost money will be made up for by rationing. Media types have picked up on the cues, but legislators and the Administration continue to deny it.

Rather than fight the inevitable, we should direct our energies to designing and lobbying for a form of rationing that Americans might be able to live with.

Perhaps it's a matter of definition.

There are two broad kinds of rationing, empirical and clinical. Empirical is numbers-based; clinical is judgment-based. The difference is a matter of emphasis. There's a lot of judgment in empirical rationing, and a lot of background numbers in clinical rationing. We'll talk about numbers-based rationing in this chapter, judgment-based rationing in the next.

Rationing has a terrible reputation. The very word conjures up images of vulnerable old women dying from disease that could be stopped if only the hard-hearted bureaucrats would approve the treatment. We hear stories of Canadian and English people dying of colon cancer that could have been cured, if only colonoscopies were as available there as they are here. We may even know of British Seniors who are confined to bed or a wheelchair in excruciating pain because they can't get approved for hip or knee replacements. All this in some of the most economically developed countries on Earth.

To make matters worse, people are beginning to notice that rationing is a conceptual relative of "eugenics," the practice of promoting a healthy society by (among other efforts) diverting care from the old and frail to the young and vigorous. Eugenics brings to the American mind horrible images of brown-shirted Nazis herding millions of Jews, Catholics, Gays, and people with disabilities into the gas chambers of the Third Reich.

No one in America is talking about Nazi eugenics. And only a handful are talking about Canadian or, worse, English rationing. But as we shall see in a moment, some form of rationing is inevitable. Rather than fight the inevitable, we should direct our energy to designing and lobbying for a form of rationing that Americans might be able to live with (no pun intended).

> *"The federal budget is on an unsustainable path, primarily because of the rising cost of health care."*
> *Congreesional Budget Office*[1]

Why More Rationing Is Inevitable

Economists will tell you that the best-case scenario for healthcare reform would reduce the growth rate in healthcare costs by 1.5% per year. Professor Christina Romer, President Obama's chief economic advisor, says that goal will not be easy to achieve. The frightening thing is that other experts project that the 1.5% goal is only half of what's really needed Growth in healthcare costs would need to be slowed, they say, by *3 percentage points a year for a period of 75 years* to stabilize the debt-to-GDP (Gross Domestic Product) ratio just for health care costs.

Even without including recent controversial federal expenditures, the "fiscal gap"—the difference between revenues and outlays -- stands at 9% of GDP. What this means is that in order to restore fiscal balance, Congress will have to increase taxes by *9% of GDP into the indefinite future.*

In a normal year, the government collects about 9% of GDP in taxes. So we're talking about doubling taxes just to cover this one "fiscal gap," without considering any additional spending from paying the White House light bill to feeding the troops to funding the "stimulus packages."

Because of economic-stimulus spending, the 2009 budget deficit is expected to reach about $1.85 trillion, or 13.1% of GDP. The Congressional Budget Office believes that the deficit will still be building at more than $1 trillion a year till 2019. That's a cumulative total increase of $10 trillion dollars. It was only in October, 2008, that the total deficit first hit $10 trillion, so we're talking about doubling the federal deficit in a short ten year period of time. In straight English, the depressing news is that the government's unfunded obligation to

> *Congress' unfunded obligation to Social Security, Medicare, and Medicaid – forget about nursing home payments – amounts to $483,000 per American household.*
>
> *The Economist, June 13, 2009*

Social Security and Medicare – not including nursing home care – is equivalent to a debt of $483,000 per household.[2]

That's why more rationing is inevitable.

Free-Market Rationing

People need all kinds of things to live a decent life: Food, clothing, housing, transportation, entertainment, and so forth. But very few people have the unlimited means to purchase as much as they want of all these things. They have to budget. People buy the cars they can afford and still have money to buy the other things they need and want. They weigh their car needs and desires against their other needs and desires, and decide how best to spend the money they have.[3]

Many people argue that it should be the same with health care: Among all the things you need and want, you decide what's most important to you, divide up your money, buy what you can afford, and live with the decision. That's how the free-market works.

This view, that all forms of rationing are variants of free-market rationing, should make rationing more acceptable to advocates of free-market systems.

"Moral Hazard"

It's curious that we don't expect cars to be free for the taking, or a lawyer's time, or any other scarce goods or services. But we expect health care to be free, or almost so. The culprit, or one of the culprits, is health insurance.

For all its benefits, health insurance, including Medicare and Medicaid, has a major downside: It distances consumers from the true cost of healthcare.

People pay the insurance premium (usually with help from their employers) and never again think about cost, save for minor co-payments and deductibles and the occasional exclusion. Just like tax-withholding keeps people from noticing the real amount of income tax they're paying – Imagine if you had to write one check a year to IRS for the full amount of your taxes! – health insurance keeps people from noticing the true costs of medicines and treatments.

We don't expect cars to be free, but we expect healthcare to be free, or nearly so.

This leads to what economists call "moral hazard": People don't make thoughtful judgments about healthcare expenditures.[4] They demand everything available, no matter what the real cost. Much of the time, they don't even know the real cost. Moral hazard is one of the principal reasons health care costs keep rising.

Uninsured Americans

The people at the short end of the free-market stick are the poor and uninsured. They have to rely on Medicaid or charity services, and often wind up with delayed diagnoses and inferior care. This is what the push for universal health insurance is all about (plus some additional profits for health-insurance companies).

Medicare pretty much takes care of the problem for people over 65. It also takes care of some five million people under 65 who are totally and permanently disabled.[5] Many experts would like to expand Medicare, so the government program for the elderly becomes the government program for everybody.[6]

For perspective, we should mention that sizeable portions of the 45 million uninsured people the politicians are talking about are foreign nationals, illegal immigrants, or native-borns who, following Fuchs, have decided that it's more important for them to buy a house or speedboat than to carry health insurance.[7]

Rationing by Government

During the 1970's, in order to try to reduce waste and overlap, some state governments introduced a variety of new regulations into the medical arena. The most controversial was the certificate-of-need program (CON) – Before a new hospital could be built, or an old one expanded, the proponents had to demonstrate that the construction was really necessary. CONs sound good, but they were never very successful.[8] The same restrictions still apply to nursing-home construction and expansion.

State governments also tried to cut costs by regulating prices. But when regulators reduced Medicaid reimbursement too far, the doctors refused to take Medicaid patients -- another form of rationing.

Rationing in Managed Care

Among the most dramatic changes introduced by Health Maintenance Organizations (HMOs) was a change in the way physicians were paid: "Capitation" rather than fee-for-service, that is, up-front payments based on the nature and size of the caseload. The key idea was that doctors could keep more money if they kept a cap on spending. They could even earn bonuses if they reduced costs far enough.

HMOs also contracted with drug experts to come up with lists of approved drugs, called "formularies." Patients who used drugs from those lists paid a very low co-payment, maybe $10; people who used other drugs paid a much higher co-payment.[9] Sometimes the HMO simply refused to pay for certain unproven or especially expensive drugs.

> *What we see just around the corner is a far more pervasive and intrusive rationing program than most of us have ever imagined.*

The predictable effect was a decrease in medical spending – and a de facto increase in rationing.

Empirical Rationing

What we see just around the corner is a far more pervasive and intrusive rationing program than most of us have ever imagined: Soon, central committees (as in England) or local committees (as in Sweden) will be busy parceling out healthcare according to sometimes objective, sometimes subjective, sometimes even *politicized* criteria.

Already medical committees in this country routinely decide who gets a heart, lung, or kidney transplant, and who gets palliative care versus the full treatment of which the institution is capable.

Cost/Effectiveness

At least in theory, all empirical rationing decisions are made on the basis of some form of cost/effectiveness.[10] In the abstract, the question is: Is this medication or treatment worth the money? This is a perfectly reasonable question, long overdue. But it's a hard concept to accept if you don't know what care costs, and if you've been accustomed to getting any kind and amount of healthcare any time you want it. In the U.S., only Oregon has tried to put such a system into practice.

Quality-Adjusted Life-Years – QALY's

Originally the cost-effectiveness question used "life years" as the criterion: How many added years of life does this drug or procedure provide, at what cost?

> *How many added years of life does this drug or procedure provide, at what cost?*

Because *quality* of life is often more important than quantity, especially for older people, most researchers have replaced life years with QALYs, *quality-adjusted* life-years. Needing just a cane to get around signifies a higher-quality life than needing a wheelchair.

The idea is for researchers to make a long list of malady/treatment combinations, and arrange them from the most cost/effective to the least. These lists might have anywhere from 500 to 1,000 entries. Then the officials estimate how many instances of each malady/treatment occur in their area in a given year, and see how far the budget will stretch. They draw a line somewhere on the list to show the cut off – malady/treatments above the line they'll pay for; those below the line, they won't.

Appendix A shows, from the 2009 Oregon healthcare priority list, excerpts that should be of particular interest to Seniors. In that list, gallbladder cancer, macular degeneration, and osteoarthritis sit well above the cut-off line, that is, they are paid for, while ruptured knee joints, renal failure from cirrhosis, and phlebitis sit below the line, that is, not paid for.

The healthcare scholars with whose work we are familiar all present empirical rationing as a binary yes/no decision: You either qualify for the treatment or you don't. We suggest that the decision could just as well be graded: The further the prescribed malady/treatment is below the (adjusted) cut-off, the larger a portion of the cost the patient would have to pay. Or, in another version, the closer the patient is to death, the larger her share of the cost should be, because she wouldn't be getting as much benefit as a person further from death would get.

Canada

The results of QALY rationing in Canada have both a positive side and a negative side:[11]

> [On the positive side, Canada] spends about 40 percent less per capita on health care [than the US does], yet every Canadian is covered, copayments are nil, and Canadians are just as healthy as or healthier than Americans.
>
> Just imagine what we could do with a 40% savings!
>
> [On the negative side,] Canadians... have to wait slightly longer than Americans for a [primary care] appointment.

> Once patients get to a [primary care physician's] office the real waiting begins. Canadians have a difficult time getting referrals to specialists, often waiting two weeks or longer (versus a few days in the United States). Once they get to their specialists, Canadians may have to wait several months or more for tests and procedures that can be obtained on demand in the United States (though perhaps after a few hassles from HMOs).

Informal reports on the Canadian experience are far less sanguine. In addition, opponents of rationing are peppering the airways with stories of people who've lived in pain for months or even years, waiting for a hip replacement.

England

Rationing in England has produced a far less costly system than ours, but with much more limited health care.[12]

> About 11 million Britons are currently on waiting lists for hospital care, with the average wait for admission approaching four months. Nearly 50,000 patients must wait a year or more to get into a hospital. Once admitted, they may never get access to some high-tech services that are commonly available in the United States and elsewhere, such as MRIs or open-heart surgery.... Britons often must wait hours just to get into emergency rooms. After finally getting into a hospital, patients may have to go on another waiting list for home care or a nursing home bed....

Horror stories abound about the English system as well, regarding, for example, people who had to wait so long for colonoscopies or MRI's that their disease, when finally discovered, was too advanced for treatment.

Oregon

In the U.S., Oregon has been the pioneer in applying QALY's to health care rationing. Dranove[13] describes the zig-zag path Oregon traveled in its effort to apply QALY thinking to its healthcare problem. The most recent Oregon list of maladies and treatments is the result of a three-way conflict – science versus politics versus media sensationalism. That conflict produced a list that lacks the scientific rigor (or rigidity) of the U.K. lists but still works reasonably well.

> *You can be sure if an American rationing plan prohibited privately purchased supplementary insurance, Black Markets would immediately develop.*

As you can imagine, there's enormous debate about the QALY approach to rationing, and lots of effort to try to improve the measures. The biggest trick is to assess quality of life meaningfully. Nevertheless, this is the approach medical boards take when saddled with making rationing decisions. They list all the drugs and procedures, compare those to the added quality and quantity of life they will produce, and decide which are worth the price.[14]

Supplementary "Rati-Gap" Health Insurance

People who can afford it can generally buy private insurance to cover disease and injuries that are below their region's cut-off, or help them get care in some part of the world where care isn't rationed, like Bangkok. But some plans prohibit the purchase of private insurance because it gives people who can afford it an advantage over people who can't.

You can be sure if an American plan prohibited privately purchased supplementary health insurance, two Black Markets would immediately develop: First, some American doctors and allied health personnel would start supplying care out of their basements, and, second, Bangkok, Singapore, and Bangalore would become even more popular "tourist" destinations than they are now.

In summary, Empirical Rationing, represented by Canada's, England's, and Oregon's rationing systems, is based on quantitative studies of the cost/effectiveness of healthcare procedures and medications. The underlying question is, Does this procedure or medication benefit the patient enough that it's worth the cost? Patient benefit is defined in terms of "life years," how much longer will the procedure or medication allow the patient to live, or, better, *quality-adjusted* life years, how much longer will it allow the patient to live a decent-quality life. Many scholars who study rationing seem to believe that Empirical Rationing is the wave of the future.

Our next chapter will talk about an established alternative to Empirical Rationing.

Chapter 11

Clinical Rationing

In the last chapter we outlined the most systematic efforts to ration drugs and treatments, what Dranove[1] calls "rational rationing." Life-Year and Quality-Adjusted Life-Year (QALY) systems are used by national, regional, and local medical committees, so far almost entirely outside the U.S., to decide which treatments they will pay for, and which they won't. In this chapter we'll talk about the more subjective efforts that are already widely used in the U.S. To get a deeper sense for how Clinical Rationing works, we'll ask you to try your hand at making some realistic rationing decisions.

Clinical Rationing

Clinical rationing is central to "physician bedside rationing," that is, rationing decisions by the patient's own doctor who presumably knows much more about the patient, her history, her future, and her family than any committee. Often but not always, clinical rationing takes into account the patient's wishes (e.g., living

> *Many Americans prefer a blend of Empirical and Clinical Rationing.*

will) and her family's.

Clinical judgment sometimes enters into Empirical Rationing, as when a particular patient is just below the cut-off line and the decision-makers are reluctant to withhold medication or treatment. It's also possible, but ethically and legally riskier, to use clinical judgment to deny treatment when the patient is above the cut-off.

Surveys show that many people like having rationing rules spelled out and public – the empirical approach -- while other people prefer that their own physicians make any rationing decisions, and that the rules give the doctor some wiggle room – the clinical approach.[2]

This and the following chapter will give you a sense of how the clinical approach to rationing works. Envision yourself a physician (or a lay member of a rationing board) whose responsibility it is to decide who gets a particular medicine or treatment, and who doesn't. Doctors are surely pondering many of the same things as they make their bedside decisions.

When you're looking at a particular case, you'll always have less information to work with than you'd like, just the approximate QALY ranking from the last chapter, some biographical information about particular patients, and your professional (and perhaps personal) knowledge of that patient. More than the QALY approach, this approach considers the patients themselves, not just the diagnosis and treatment.

Six Kinds of Rationing

In this brave new world of rationing, there are at least six distinct rationing techniques:[3]

Denial, the yes/no decision that we automatically think of when we hear the word "rationing."

Exclusion, which means excluding whole segments of the population, e.g., illegal aliens, people older than 75.

Dilution, ordering fewer tests, for example, and providing fewer doctors, nurses, or aides.

Deterrence, making access difficult through geographical or other road-blocks.

Delay, requiring a waiting list.

Termination, stopping a treatment that's already underway.

The Rationing Exercise

Your job as you work your way through this chapter will be to decide which, if any, of these kinds of rationing should be applied to the various patients described below. *It will require you to deny, exclude, dilute, deter, delay, or terminate medical care from people you generally think deserve more care than they're going to get*, and maybe to award care to people you think are less deserving. This is the nub of rationing – finding the right foundations for making tough decisions, even life-and-death decisions.

Decision-makers want to apply basic human virtues like compassion, generosity, and justice.

Among the factors that come to mind for making rationing decisions are:

Biographic Factors like age, sex, race, ethnicity, and religion

Social Factors like class, education, geography, and past and present value to society

Personal Factors like health habits and personality.

At the same time, decision-makers *want* to apply basic human virtues like compassion, generosity, and justice but are not always free to do so.

Instructions

Below are five sets of three patients each. At this point, your clinic has just about half the money you'd need to fund full and immediate treatment for all three of these people whose cases you are considering at the same time, generally enough to take full care of one of the three patients, partial care of maybe two. You're forced into rationing.

> What kind of rationing will you apply to whom, and why?
>
> What factors do you find most compelling, in favor of or against approving each individual's request for full and immediate treatment?
>
> What factors other than the strictly medical are you tempted to use to help you make your rationing decision?

Set One

Patient 1: Everybody loved Harriet. A bright and lively 60, she was kind, out-going, and generous. With the help of her husband, Fred, she had foster-mothered 24 ghetto children over the years, and she led the alto section of Ebeneezer Baptist Church since she and Fred joined thirty years ago. Life became more difficult when Fred died last year, still more difficult recently when Harriet was diagnosed with kidney disease, headed rapidly toward renal failure. With regular dialysis, he doctors told her, she could live another ten years, maybe more. Without it, the best she could hope for was three to six months. Renal dialysis is slightly below the QALY cut-off for Harriet's part of the country,

Patient 2: Gladys was as unassuming a woman as you could imagine. The few people who had known her at First Presbyterian knew little about her. For most of her 93 years, she was pretty much a recluse. She was no less reclusive now, in her eighth year in Blessed Mary's Home for Seniors. Until recently, all she needed was custodial care, because it had become hard for her to take care of her basic needs. Even at that, her stay in the home had consumed all the family's assets. Three months ago the doctors found a brain tumor that, to Gladys' relief, turned out to be benign. But the doctors said it could turn malignant, and, in any event, was going to cause her a great deal of pain starting soon. They recommended surgery to remove it. Brain surgery for benign tumors is well below the applicable QALY cut-off.

Patient 3: Reuben was as tough as they come. Seventy-six and retired, he was, if anything, crustier than he had been when he was working. A retired trial lawyer, he was used to getting his own way, or "getting even" if he didn't. His in-your-face style did not endear him to the staff at the Shalom Home, as it hadn't endeared him to his three former wives. His frame of mind wasn't improved by a recent diagnosis of anal cancer. His doctors recommended immediate surgery, with a follow-up course of radiation and chemotherapy. To delay, they insisted, was to risk his comfort, indeed his life. This surgery is just above the QALY cut-off.

Questions for Set One

What kind(s) of rationing would you apply? Whose request would you refuse, in part or in whole? Anybody's? Everybody's?

What factors do you find most persuasive, in favor of or against approving full and immediate treatment?

Are you tempted to favor one person over another for other than strictly medical reasons?

In particular, would changing race, religion, sex, or age make a difference in your decision?

Would Harriet's history as a kind and generous woman influence you?

How about Reuben's history as a hard and egotistical lawyer?

Set Two

Patient 4: Indira, now 68, had the misfortune to be crossing the street at the wrong time, and was run over by a drunk driver. The accident left her bedridden, with significant brain damage. The driver, of course, had no insurance and no assets; indeed, the Court found him guilty of reckless driving and DUI and sentenced him to two years in prison.

Indira was fully aware of what was going on around her, but she had a desperately hard time remembering much of anything in the near term, even the names of her grandchildren. She recently developed congestive heart failure. With treatment, her prognosis is good; without, guarded at best. Treatment for congestive heart failure is well above the QALY cut-off.

Patient 5: Buster, 72, was the driver of the car that ruined Indira's life. He had gotten a dozen DUI tickets before he ran her down. People who knew the situation were appalled that he was still behind the wheel.

Near the end of his first year in prison, the doctors discovered a tumor in his left lung. Even with his history of drinking, the specialists said a transplant would probably solve the problem, and predicted that the surgery would be successful. They reminded the prison authorities that a federal judge had issued an order that prisoners receive the same medical care that citizens in general receive, regardless of cost. Lung transplants are below the applicable QALY cut-offs.

Patient 6: Shortly after Silas, her husband, died, Bertha, 79, tried unsuccessfully to kill herself. Her yardman found her unconscious in a garage full of carbon monoxide. She had written a note explaining that she didn't want to wait any longer to reunite with Silas. Now she lies in bed all day, staring blankly at the ceiling.

The family has asked the doctors to pull the plug, but one of them said it's too early, there's some chance that Bertha will recover at least some of her sensibilities. In the meantime, she needs custodial care in a nursing home and will surely require more and more treatment as time goes on. At $8,000 a month and rising, it won't be long till the house and all her savings are used up, and she goes onto Medicaid

Questions for Set Two

What would you decide about rationing for these three people? What factors influenced you?

In particular, would Buster's role in Indira's condition influence your decision, keeping the court order in mind? How about Bertha's brain-damaged state?

Set Three

Patient 7: Helen, a young 89, had been married to a lawyer. Many years ago, the two of them set up a trust arrangement to protect their assets from long-term health care costs. The trust gave her enough income to be comfortable and kept her house, their retirement plan, and their savings and investment accounts out of the reach of the government. Her three grandchildren are using the family money to pay their way through private colleges, to get started on lucrative careers, and to have a little fun.

After her husband died, Helen lived successfully in the family home, with help from a housekeeper, a handyman, and Meals-on-Wheels. Eventually it became clear to everyone that she needed more care than these good people could provide, so she moved into a nursing home with a wonderful view of the mountains. Her expenses are running around $8,000 a month, plus whatever it will take in the future to handle her worsening diabetes, which could easily double the present cost. In about a year she'll have to ask Medicaid to take over her nursing-home expenses, and her diabetes treatments. At least for now, her diabetes treatments are well above the QALY cut-offs, although her age is an issue.

Patient 8: By most people's standards, Bernice was a wealthy woman. She and her husband were accustomed to the finer things of life and, more important, used to taking care of themselves. But things eventually reached the point where her Parkinson's (and his dementia) made it too tough for them to live on their own. So they moved into a top-notch nursing home in an exclusive part of town. There they lived as well as one can in a three-bedroom suite – their favorite furniture from the big house, fresh flowers every few days, elegant luncheons in the dining room, and more.

Two things bothered Harriet: First, she saw a TV program that said rich people shouldn't be allowed to buy better care than anybody else, even if it was their own money. That made her feel guilty and scared. Second, she began to wonder just how long, at $25,000 a month, their money would last. Not more than two or three years, she guessed. While the doctors warned her not to expect too much from her Parkinson's and his Alzheimer's treatments, both treatments were well above the QALY cut-offs.

Patient 9: Gladys and Bill were a well-off, not wealthy, upper-middle class couple, she a teacher, he a successful life insurance salesman. Now that Gladys was in a nursing home, she appreciated how cautious Bill had been with their money. One of the things she especially appreciated was that he insisted they buy a long-term care insurance policy, with pretty high daily limits and a five-year payout period. Trouble is she's been in the home nearly five years, and she's been wondering where the money's going to come from next year. All this worry wasn't helping her hypertension and heart disease, the treatment for which was well above the QALY cut-off.

Questions for Set Three

What factors do you find most persuasive, in favor of or against approving full and immediate treatment? Any factors beyond the strictly medical?

How about socioeconomic factors?

In particular, should Helen's kids take over her expenses, because they're getting the lion's share of her estate? Indeed, should they reimburse Medicaid for funds it already spent on her?

Should Harriet be prevented from using her money to live so well when other people live so poorly?

Who should pay for Gladys' care when her insurance runs out?

Set Four

Patient 10: Lawrence was diagnosed with Type II diabetes when he was 65. Before that, he'd never met a doughnut he didn't like. After the diagnosis, he fought every day to keep his blood sugar under control. As his father had struggled with alcohol, he struggled with carbohydrates. Lawrence lost more food battles than he won, and now, twenty years later, was exhibiting all the signs of advancing diabetes, especially problems with his feet.

The nursing home expenses had long ago consumed the last of his assets, and now he was totally the government's responsibility. Room, board, and special treatment were costing Medicaid more than $150,000 a year, and likely to increase. The course of treatment for his diabetes was slightly below the applicable QALY cut-off.

Patient 11: There's no polite way to put it: Harry was a drunk. Not a day went by that he didn't consume at least half a bottle of cheap whiskey, or a couple of six-packs. When he was younger, he tried to break the grip alcohol had on him, but as time went by his efforts became more and more feeble. He lost his job as a machinist and now made a meager living as a low-level handyman and occasional laborer. Alcoholism combined with renal failure was costing Medicaid a little over $12,000 a month. Treatment for end-stage renal failure was below the QALY cut-off.

Patient 12: Jim started smoking back on the farm, when he was 12. For most of his adult life he consumed three packs of Camel straights a day, more if he was under stress. He was aware of the risks – who wasn't? – but cigarettes were his best friends, and he was loath to give them up.

Not until he was well into his 70's was there, except for a little shortness of breath, any significant health problem. At 78, the docs found cancer in his right lung and suggested a transplant. Jim thought it was a capital idea, especially since Medicaid would be responsible for the $250,000 bill. Lung transplants are well below the QALY cut-off.

Questions for Set Four

In particular, should Lawrence's history with sweets influence your decision? Or Harry's with whiskey? Or Jim's with tobacco?

To what extent should bad behavior affect rationing decisions? Do we really know enough about addictions to use them when the outcome will be life – or death?

Set Five

Patient 13: Esther was a career criminal. She had started with simple shop-lifting as a teen, grew into embezzling as an adult, but made her mark in her later years as a cocaine dealer. As she always said, dealing coke has a better risk/reward ratio that any other business she knew. She lived large, and got a kick out of her recent reputation as the "Canny Granny."

Six months ago her world collapsed when she was

diagnosed with ALS, Lou Gehrig's Disease. The doctors were frank about it. Her locomotion, speech, and breathing would all degenerate. She could choose curative care, palliative care, or perhaps a combination. They'd all be expensive. At best, she'd have five years to live, an increasingly awful five years.

She wanted to take a crack at beating the disease, but ALS/curative was below the QALY cut-off. She had no savings or investment accounts, no house, no other assets – at least none that anybody could find. So she turned to Medicaid for help,

Patient 14: Carmella gave up her lucrative nurse-anesthetist career when she was 45 and became a lay missionary in Tanzania, Africa. She loved her work and the locals she worked with, thrived in the bush hospitals, and, though she'd never have said it out loud, resented it deeply when her doctor sent her home because she contracted a bizarre tropical disease.

The disease didn't respond to any therapy the American doctors could figure out, not even the tropical-disease specialists at the Mayo Clinic, and Carmella started slowly wasting away, entering a nursing home just after her 60th birthday. The doctors were at a loss; they tried one procedure after another, with limited success at best. Last year, Medicaid paid $7,500 a month for the room, board, and general care, and now the doctors were predicting that those costs would triple. The doctors figured she'd live another 10-12 years, increasingly dependent, increasingly uncomfortable, eventually immobile and in excruciating pain. Her disease barely had a name, to say nothing of a QALY ranking. But it was rare, and the doctors knew treatment would be expensive.

Whom would you trust to make rationing decisions if you were the patient?

Patient 15: Vivianne had been a very successful call girl in her youth, the kind who can provide what customers called a real "girl-friend experience" – for $1,500 a night. Her remarkable income kept her very comfortable and relatively content (if not actually happy) until the day her doctor told her she was HIV-positive.

She responded pretty well to the therapeutic cocktail her doctors prescribed, and to the diet-and-exercise program; but nevertheless she became weaker and weaker. With her immune defenses diminishing by the day, she fell victim to one disease after another, but none of them killed her. The doctors were amazed. It looked like she was going to beat the odds. It looked like she'd be around for a long time, a very expensive time. Owing to a very effective lobbying campaign, AIDS treatment is above the QALY cut-off.

Questions for Set Five

How would you weigh Esther's and Vivianne's career histories against Carmella's? Esther's against Vivianne's? How much do those histories matter to you?

Reflection

Now that you've tried your hand at it, how do you feel about rationing? Whom would you trust to make rationing decisions if you were the patient – A governmental rationing board? Your personal physician? Your spouse or children or neighbors? Anybody else?

Would you prefer the QALY approach described in the previous chapter, or the more personal approach described here – Empirical Rationing or Clinical Rationing?

What would it take to make the process better? To prevent bias and other injustice?

How do you feel now about the choice between paying dramatically higher taxes versus submitting to a medical rationing system?

Review

Let's take a closer look at the material from this chapter. This time around, however, let's frame the decisions as explicitly ethical questions: What we need to think about is, Is this the right thing to do?

Is it the right thing to do, to parcel out medicine and medical treatment partly on the basis of biographic, social, and personal factors?

Biographic Factors

Let's look at the biographic factors first, one at a time – age, sex, race, ethnicity, and religion.

Age. The first factor many people think of when they're thinking about rationing is age:

"She's had a long and satisfying life."

"It's time for her to let go."

"It's all downhill from here."

In fact, some authors have even proposed a flat rationing rule: No medical treatments (other than palliative) for anybody over 75, or maybe 80, because they're no longer contributing to society. Period.[4]

Age cut-offs make sense, until you start thinking about the Seniors you know who are living happy and satisfying lives. *Is it the right thing to do,* to make a flat no-treatment-after-age-X rule?

For that matter, is it the right thing to do to insist that people "contribute to society" until they're dead? What about simply enjoying one's Golden Years? Isn't that part of the American Way of Life?

What about people who disciplined themselves throughout their lives, so they'd be fit in old age. Should they now be deprived of the healthcare they need? How ironic would that be?

Hold that thought for a minute.

Sex. When you made your rationing decisions above, did you find yourself feeling a little more sympathetic toward the women than the men? Most people do. For better or for worse, in our culture many people see women, especially older women, as more vulnerable and deserving of some degree of preference. Is this a good thing, or a bad thing?

In addition, women live longer on average than men. Some people view this as an unfair financial advantage to women; others view it as a disadvantage.

Furthermore, women tend to have messier and more expensive health problems.

Should rationing therefore be stricter for women than for men?

Hold that thought too.

Race, Ethnicity, and Religion. These are still some of the most sensitive topics in American society. Because they're so sensitive people don't talk very much about how those factors influence their assessments of other people. Consider an elderly Black woman – Are rationing committee members more likely to support her because of our history of discrimination against Blacks? That is, will they practice affirmative action? Or are they likely to vote against her because she's Black and therefore (they think) less worthy? Will they practice racism?

How about a Moslem woman – Would she be unfairly disadvantaged if her medical needs were up against those of a Jew or a Christian?

How about an atheist?

Now, why do we keep attaching that annoying postscript – *"Hold that thought"* – to the paragraphs about biographic factors? Simple: Because these are factors we all think about and that one way or another probably influence our decisions – but to use them in such decisions may be illegal, even unconstitutional! The ink won't be dry on any order based on age, sex, race, ethnicity, or religion before people will sue to have the order quashed.

In some parts of the country, you can add to the list of prohibited considerations sexual orientation, welfare status, and more.

It's possible that the courts will eventually decide, as they decided in the University of Michigan affirmative action cases,[5] that these factors can be used, so long as none of them is the sole and principal reason for the decision. Like race in college admissions, age, sex, race, ethnicity, and maybe even religion will perhaps be usable in healthcare rationing decisions, as long as they are among a dozen or more factors that every committee will consider.

The ink won't be dry on any order based on sex, race, ethnicity, religion – maybe even age! – before people will sue to have the order quashed.

In a similar vein, the Americans with Disabilities Act (ADA) provides special protections for individuals with disabilities. While neither "frail" nor "elderly" constitutes a disability, specific physical or cognitive impairments may be disabilities. So people with Alzheimer's and other cognitive disorders and people whose activities of daily life are substantially impeded may enjoy the special protections of this legislation, which might preclude any application of rationing. This is uncharted territory in law and could throw a wrench into a rationing plan.

You can count on a lot of scholarly debate and court action on these matters.

Social Factors

Social factors include social status, geography, and past or present value to society.

Social Status. All else equal, whose plea for medical care would you grant – That of a governor recently diagnosed with

Alzheimer's, or that of a handyman similarly diagnosed? How about a CEO versus his or her secretary? Or a TV star versus her or his housekeeper?

There's also reason to believe that healthy living correlates with social class, with the lower classes engaging in more bad habits like smoking, drinking, and eating too much sugar, fat, and salt.

On a still broader scale, because the upper classes – or maybe it's the middle classes -- have contributed more to society than the lower classes, should rationing be more generous for the upper classes, more strict for the lower?

Geography. Some parts of the country are more dangerous than others. Living in the ghetto is riskier than living in the suburbs. Living on a farm is riskier than living in town. Living in New Jersey is riskier than living in Minnesota. The rationing question is, Should rationing be more strict for people who live in more dangerous places? After all, it was largely their choice to live there… wasn't it?

Should an archbishop with Alzheimer's get treatment preference over a homeless man with the same disease?

Geography sometimes connects with socio-economic class. On a national level, does it matter if you're from Florida or Idaho? California or Maine? Hawaii or Alaska? On a local level, how about Manhattan versus The Bronx? A metropolitan area or a rural area?

As long as these factors aren't surrogates – hidden substitutes – for the forbidden factors we talked about, committees are free to use them. But you have to be careful that "Manhattan versus The Bronx" isn't code for "White versus Black."

Past or Present Value to Society. Should an archbishop with Alzheimer's get treatment preference over a homeless man with the same level of the same disease, all else equal? To this question there's an immediate chorus of answers, half yelling "No, everybody's equal"; half yelling "Yes, otherwise why does the archbishop get to wear the special hat?"

Should disabled people be disadvantaged because they might not be contributing as much as they used to, or as much as other people do now? What does it mean to "contribute to society"? Does a child contribute as much as an adult? A girl as much as a boy? A husband as much as his wife? The husband as much as his boss, or his doctor, or his confessor? The businessman or –woman as much as the monk or nun? There are few questions as philosophically messy as trying to distinguish among people according to their value.

Personal Factors

Personal Factors include health habits and likeability.

Health Habits. In the face of this generation's obsession with health and healthful eating, it's not at all surprising that some people are insisting that smokers who won't give up smoking, drinkers who won't give up drinking, and obese people who won't give up over-eating don't deserve health care, particularly not health care paid for by the rest of society.

But do we really know enough about why people do things that aren't good for them? It would be a lot easier to understand people if Rational Choice Theory worked – but it doesn't! People are sometimes rational, often times not. The question is why.

Likeability. It's so much easier to be generous to a likeable person than to a nasty one, a jerk. Should likeability be a factor in parceling out healthcare?

We're entering a new "Age of the Gene." Nearly every week *Nature* magazine reports some new discovery, a gene that determines this, a strand of DNA that influences that.

The point is, if our health habits, likeability, and other inclinations are substantially influenced by factors beyond our control – heredity – then *is it the right thing to do,* to use those to ration health care?

One of the great debates of the 21st century will be that between free will and determinism.

To summarize, Clinical Rationing is much more personal than Empirical Rationing. It rests on the relationship between patient and physician, a combination of the patient's wishes and the physician's understanding of the patient's history, condition, and diagnosis, with due attention to the desires of the patient's family. In many ways, Clinical Rationing is more humane than Empirical Rationing, but it's also more vulnerable to abuse. In a later chapter we will argue that Clinical Rationing *informed by Empirical Rationing,* is the approach to rationing most likely to be acceptable to the American people. But we can't do that until we examine some of the key ethical issues surrounding rationing.

If personal characteristics are influenced by genetics, is it right to use them to ration healthcare?

Chapter 12

Ethical Issues in Rationing

Ethical Principles

Ethical considerations should play a central role in any search for a distinctly American rationing plan. Philosophers down the ages and around the world have suggested many general principles. We'll adopt three of them:

> *Behave in such a way that what you do could become a universal moral law.*
> *Immanuel Kant (1785)*

The Golden Rule: Do unto others as you would have them do unto you;

The Utilitarian Principle: Do the greatest good for the greatest number of people;

The Categorical Imperative: Behave in such a way that what you do could become a universal moral law.

The Golden Rule, or "the ethic of reciprocity," is the most ancient and widespread of all the ethical principles, tracing its origins to ancient Egypt and figuring prominently in Buddhism, Christianity, Confucianism, Islam, Judaism, Taoism, and other religions. Its negative version – *Do not do to others,* etc. – is sometimes called the Silver Rule. Another variant – *Do unto others as they would like to be done by* – is called the Platinum Rule.[1]

A handful of serious philosophers (and some wags) have criticized the Golden Rule principally because people have different tastes and we can't generally know how they would like to be treated.

Nevertheless, the Golden Rule remains a useful guide to behaving ethically

The Utilitarian Principle – *Seek the greatest happiness for the greatest number* – first appeared in John Stewart Mills' *Utilitarianism* (1861) which itself is rooted in Epicurus' philosophy of the happy life (300BC).[2]

Kant's Categorical Imperative, or required principle of behavior, comes in several versions, the most popular of which is the first, which we loosely render as: *Behave in such a way that what you do could become a universal moral law.*[3]

Applications of the Principles

In the preceding chapters there seem to be three categories of difficult ethical questions: Those that have to do with the principle of rationing itself, those that have to do with the criteria for rationing, and those that have to do with a special form of rationing, euthanasia. As illustration, we'll apply each of the ethical principles to a question from each category.

The Principle of Rationing

Is it the right thing to do, to deprive some people of needed healthcare in order to keep other people's taxes affordable?

The ethical answer to this question turns on the definitions of "needed" and "affordable." Let's suppose "needed" really means "convenient" and "affordable" means, "If taxes go any higher, my boss is going to close our department and I'm going to lose my job."

Do unto others.... Surely you wouldn't want your own convenience to cost someone else his job. It would be considerably less of an ethical problem if his losing his job were merely to inconvenience you. So Seniors should not demand treatments which, together, produce really bad consequences for younger people.

Seek the greatest happiness.... If a relatively small number of people desire a convenient medical procedure that would cause the taxes of many people to rise dramatically, the former should yield to the latter. So Seniors wanting minor – "convenient" – treatments should pay for those themselves if those treatments would result in substantial tax increases for people in general. So the Golden Rule and the Utilitarian Principle lead us to the same conclusion.

How about the Categorical Imperative, which many philosophers view as the most demanding of the moral principles?

Behave so what you do could become a moral law. Surely it should not be a moral principle that the convenience of a few should result in severe problems for the many. Again, Seniors should eschew minor treatments if those would result in substantially increased taxation.

Same result. But the question wasn't all that difficult.

Let's reverse the weights so the "needed" healthcare would make the difference between life and death, and the "affordable" tax increase is one beyond which people will only be deprived of some consumer goods, like an expanded wardrobe or a summer vacation. The conclusions will, of course, change dramatically.

Do unto others.... Surely you would be willing to give up some consumer goods so someone else could receive potentially life-saving treatment, and would expect them to act the same way toward you.

Seek the greatest happiness for the greatest number. Here the Greatest Happiness Principle becomes fuzzy, because we have a great good for a small number of people versus a small good for a great number of people. Which condition does the principle require us to follow? It doesn't say.

We're inclined to prefer the larger good for the small number of people, in which case the two principles again come to the same conclusion.

Behave so what you do could become a moral law. Certainly it could be a general ethical principle that we should cause even a very large number of people some deprivation of consumer goods in return for providing a small number the life-saving care they need. So it's better to raise everybody's taxes somewhat than to withhold life-saving treatments from others. The three principles all lead to this conclusion: Rationing is ethical until the burden on the general population becomes onerous.[4]

> *This line of thinking supports the Oregon rationing system.*

Everything here turns on the consequences of the tax versus the consequences of the particular treatment.

Rather to our surprise, this line of thinking seems to support the Oregon priorities, in the list of which the most serious conditions and treatments are positioned above the cut-off point, the lesser treatments, for the most part, below (Appendix A). It might even be more consistent with a graded version of the Oregon system (e.g., varying co-payments; see p. 84, above). This would be a good time to re-examine the Oregon priorities to see if any treatments below the cut-off should be moved up, or vice versa.

The Criteria for Rationing

Is it the right thing to do, to deprive people of medicine and medical treatments if their illness is the result of their own bad behavior, e.g., smoking and drinking?

The first thing we need to do is examine this question to determine whether or not the bad behaviors are really matters of free will and perverse choice. The problem here is that behavioral science is still in its infancy when it comes to understanding why people do what's bad for them.[5] Some social scientists say people are fundamentally rational; others say No, their behavior is the result of a roiling cauldron of mysterious forces. In addition, we're just beginning to understand the role of neurochemistry and neurophysiology.

All we can be sure of at this point is that human motivation isn't as simple as we used to think. Our view is that we should not be making life and death decisions on the basis of such limited knowledge. Tempting as it is, we should not let what may only be self-righteousness and stereotype color our rationing decisions.

Let's say there's a strong neurochemical basis for compulsive eating. And let's say you're lucky enough not to have inherited or otherwise developed that compulsion. Given our present limited knowledge, would you be willing to give the eater the benefit of the doubt? *Do unto others....* Does the same thinking apply to the other bad behaviors? Does it apply to personal characteristics like sex and age, and whatever connections they might have to behavioral choices?

When it comes to withholding treatment on the basis of bad behavior, what is *the greatest good?* To punish those who engaged in socially disapproved behavior? To reward those who didn't? To encourage younger people not to engage in those behaviors?

Or is discrimination on this basis simply a handy way to cull the sheep from the goats and take some pressure off the healthcare budget?

Promoting behaviors that encourage the upcoming generation not to engage in bad behaviors could be a moral maxim. So possibly could rewarding good behavior. Punishing socially unacceptable behavior cannot turn into a moral principle until we know more about why people do things that are bad for them.

Euthanasia

Is it the right thing to do, to participate in euthanasia?

The majority of philosophers and theologians oppose suicide. Their principal argument is that suicide is a permanent solution to a temporary problem, e.g., depression. Some add the theological argument that "life is not ours to give or take."

An equally compelling argument on the other side is that freedom of choice should extend to the individual's choice whether to live or die.

We suspect that the voluntary euthanasia debate will parallel the Pro Life/Pro Choice debate.[6]

The reasons people generally give for wanting to take their own lives through voluntary euthanasia range widely in importance. They include avoidance of severe physical or emotional pain, preserving their estate from high end-of-life medical expenses, feeling chronically depressed, and "just having tired of the whole thing." Preserving the estate, of course, has emotional implications for heirs that go far beyond the assets themselves, e.g., affection.[7]

The decision is complicated by the enormous potential for error and abuse. Devices and medications may fail, or may cause ugly side effects. People with an emotional or financial interest in the patient's death may push for euthanasia for their own self-interest, an especially dangerous situation in which (as in Switzerland) *lay*-assisted suicide is permitted.

> *The voluntary-euthanasia debate will parallel the abortion debate.*

But the evolving experience in Switzerland, the Netherlands, and Oregon suggests that these problems can be eliminated in most cases.[8, 9]

There are two kinds of euthanasia, voluntary and involuntary. Most of us are aware of the Inuit practice of voluntary euthanasia, in which an elder, when he or she can no longer contribute to the community, seeks out a comfortable ice floe and rides it out to sea. As long as it remains totally voluntary, such a practice seems practical, even generous.

The problem, of course, is that the Innuit practice did not always remain voluntary.

We're talking about voluntary euthanasia, in which the patient either carries out the act herself or with the assistance of a specially trained physician. As the law on this topic evolves, it's possible to envision suicide assisted by a physician's assistant, a nurse, or even a lay person, perhaps a spouse, close friend or family member under some kind of medical and legal supervision.

> *Medicine should provide people who want a painless, sure, and dignified way to end their lives the means to do so.*

Many of the tragic "murder-suicide" cases in which an aged husband kills his ailing wife and then himself are probably voluntary euthanasia cases.

Do unto others in the case of voluntary euthanasia focuses on compassion, or mercy. If I were facing a painful and expensive death, I'd want someone to help me out of my misery. And I'd willingly help them if they were in the same straits.

Greatest happiness for the greatest number is also satisfied. A painless, sure, and dignified death is certainly a form of happiness for some patients, perhaps also for their families. It is also a good for the healthcare system.

And, yes, permitting everybody who decides that it's time to end their lives to choose voluntary euthanasia could be a universal moral principle that would not damage society. Thus the *universal moral maxim* requirement is satisfied.[8]

Despite the widespread negative reaction to Dr. Jack

Kervorkian and his "suicide machine," our conclusion is that medicine should provide people who *want* to end their lives the means to do so.[9] Switzerland and the Netherlands have instituted services of this sort, as has the state of Oregon.[10]

So, if our reasoning is correct, even in the hard case of euthanasia it is possible to devise an ethical rationing system.

This line of thinking can extend to any number of questions about the principles, procedures, and effects of rationing. The important thing for our discussion is to raise the question, *Is it the right thing to do?* And to have a set of clear moral principles against which to test this question.

To summarize, in this chapter we explored the ethics of rationing systems. Trying to avoid relativism (situation ethics), we selected three widely accepted ethical principles – the Golden Rule, the Utilitarian Principle, and the Categorical Imperative – and applied them to each of three difficult rationing questions. We concluded that keeping these principles in mind will allow us to build an ethical rationing system.

Chapter 13

Third Recapitulation

To keep solvent the government's healthcare programs for aging Americans, the only choice is, To Tax or To Ration.

We're all familiar with the tax alternatives. On the federal level are income taxes, payroll taxes, excise taxes, and that European import more and more economists are talking about, the Value-Added Tax (VAT), a national sales tax.

On the state level – Bear in mind that the states pay half the Medicaid costs, a crushing burden – the possibilities include income taxes, sales taxes (including a tax on healthcare premiums or benefits) and a panoply of user fees.

Just as the federal government will surely pressure the states to come up with additional money, the states will pressure the counties and cities. This of course could mean increases in property taxes, sales taxes, and fees of one sort or another.

However, regardless of the amount and kind of tax the different levels of government may apply, there is simply not enough money in the economy to tax our way into a solvent long-term healthcare system.

That leaves rationing.

However much we may loathe and despise the idea of rationing healthcare for older Americans and however much we may fear the rationing programs that have taken hold in Canada and England, *rationing is inevitable,* and we believe that *Senior Americans will bear the brunt of it.*

This growing inclination to ration Senior citizens' healthcare more than other people's raises an interesting question. Over the years there has been a tacit agreement across the generations that older people will pay toward education even though they have no children in school, and younger people will in turn pay toward Senior healthcare even if they have no living elders. If rationing is applied disproportionately to Seniors, should those Seniors then reduce or terminate their payments toward education?

> *Rationing is inevitable, and we anticipate that aging Americans will bear the brunt of it.*

In any event, the kind of rationing we're talking about is not the relatively benign rationing that currently exists in Medicare and Medicaid and in HMO's around the country, where patients are routinely required to use a generic drug rather than the more expensive brand-name version, unproven treatments are not supported, or other controversial services are more often delayed than denied. We're talking about rationing where some authority says "No, you're too old," "No, you're too sick," or "No, you're probably going to die before we'd get our money's worth from that treatment." The treatments, medications, and services we're talking about include not only chronic and acute healthcare in general – the usual Medicare items -- but also items of special concern to elderly Americans: Knee and hip replacements (especially the second time around), end-of-life treatments and medications, even a bed in a nursing home or hospice.

We believe that rather than battle the inevitable, our time, money, and energy will be best used to design and lobby for a rationing system Americans can live with, a distinctly American rationing system.

There are two broad kinds of rationing to choose from, Empirical Rationing and Clinical Rationing. Empirical Rationing is built on cost/effectiveness data: Rank treatments from those that provide the most additional years of decent-quality life to those that provide the least, then draw a cut-off line on the list where your state's healthcare budget is likely to run out: Pay for treatments above the line; don't pay for treatments below. Oregon is the American pioneer in Empirical Rationing.

Clinical Rationing is "physician bedside rationing," in which your doctor, who presumably knows you, your medical history, your condition, and your prognosis better than anybody else, makes the decision whether or not a particular treatment is cost/effective *for you.* Surveys suggest that Americans prefer Clinical Rationing, especially when it's informed by the priority lists that come from Empirical Rationing studies.

Each kind of rationing is full to the brim with ethical questions, but the bottom line is that it is possible to design an ethical rationing system. The rest of this book will spell out what a distinctly American long-term healthcare program might look like.

Part IV
Foundation for a National Conversation --
Toward a Distinctly American Rationing Plan for Long-Term Healthcare

---

Chapter 14

Affinity Groups

In this chapter, we're going to propose a return to some of the ways of our ancestors, who seemed sometimes to know better than we how to care for their frail elderly. Though it may seem Pollyanna, we think that, under the right circumstances, this ancillary to long-term healthcare could help reduce costs *and* improve the quality of care. It can also ameliorate the pain of a formal rationing system.

It Takes a Village

If "it takes a village" to raise a child, maybe it takes a village to care for our very old neighbors, friends, and family members.[1]

Loretta's Story

Picture Loretta, a frail, elderly woman who's not among "the sickest of the sick" but is still unable to handle many of the activities of daily life.

She's mildly confused much of the time, and the confusion seems to be deepening. She's not inclined to wander, at least not yet; but she can't be trusted at the kitchen stove over which she used to spend so much time.

If she could afford it, she'd love to have home health aides in her life. She's not impoverished, but there's no way her budget could handle more than a few hours' help a week, not nearly enough. Without some special intervention, she's destined for a nursing home. She'll follow the usual path: Deplete virtually all her assets, then go onto Medicaid for the duration.

Loretta's a member of a church that, like many churches, is full of altruistic people who would like to commit to some kind of social service. She and the church members share the same values and the same social history. Almost like a family, the members celebrate their similarities and tolerate their differences. The affinity she feels with her parishioners is the key to our proposal.

Affinity Groups

Why don't the members of the church band together to provide free or very low cost at-home healthcare for Loretta? In pairs or trios members could easily cover much of Loretta's day; maybe even provide round-the-clock care if and when that becomes necessary. They could help her in so many ways – cooking, grooming, bathing, companionship, worship. They could help with the little repairs the house needs, and they could even make minor improvements for Loretta's safety and convenience. They couldn't do what it takes a physician's or nurse's license to do, but they could arrange for a public-health nurse to come by as necessary.

In short, they could build a personal helping relationship with Loretta based on their "affinity."

This is the way people used to care for their own. Indeed, some still do.

Complexion of Affinity Groups

Loretta's particular Affinity Group is a church. It could be conservative or liberal or something in between – Whatever matches her values. It might be Pro-Life or Pro-Choice, Republican or Democrat, Catholic or Protestant or Jewish or Moslem. The complexion simply wouldn't matter, so long as it complemented Loretta's values and beliefs.

> *Why don't the members of the organization band together and "adopt" a Senior?*

For that matter, the Affinity Group wouldn't have to be a religious organization. It could be a retirement home filled with 55-plussers looking for something worthwhile to do; a fraternal organization like the American Legion or the Daughters of Isabella; a professional organization like the chiropractors' association or the postal workers' union; or the alumni of a private or public school. It could be a neighborhood, a high-rise, or even a FaceBook or MySpace page. The possibilities are endless. All that's needed is affinity and altruism.

Barriers

Why aren't Affinity Groups the mode now? The main reason is not that altruism has disappeared from the American landscape or that there aren't enough instances of affinity in our modern dissociated culture. *It's that a morass of well-intentioned laws and regulations has made this kind of generosity nearly impossible.*

Among the most formidable barriers are:

Local ordinances that prohibit operating a group home in a residential neighborhood, or that prevent more than a handful of unrelated persons from living together. These ordinances would be problematic if and when more than a few frail elderly might want to share living quarters, after the fashion of the Golden Girls.

State laws that prescribe standards for "nursing homes" or "board-and-care facilities," e.g., number of nursing hours, room sizes, and innumerable fire and safety-code regulations. Affinity Group members would need to enjoy the same exceptions that are currently available for family-member care-givers. The idea would be to expand the definition of "family" to include non-traditional relationships which, in a long-term care context, fulfill the same function as a family.

Federal regulations that bear on Medicaid reimbursement, including federal regulations administered by the states. These regulations should be an issue only if the Affinity Group seeks full or partial reimbursement, in which case it will have to comply with all applicable regulations. Given the potential cost savings, federal reimbursement makes sense. However, since the federal government seems unlikely to exempt Affinity Groups from the web of nursing-home regulations, the best move would probably be for Affinity Groups to provide their services free of charge.

What Could Go Wrong?

What could go wrong with an Affinity Group committing to provide at-home care for one or more elderly persons? A handful of possibilities come to mind.

Elder abuse – emotional, financial, physical, even sexual. This seems most unlikely, but there's always the possibility. Indeed, field reports suggest that the problem is growing. Without going into gruesome detail, we envision two protections against elder abuse:[3] First, Affinity Group members always work in pairs or trios; second, there needs to be some kind of loose reporting connection with a responsible authority in the Affinity Group itself, its sponsor, or the government, e.g., Department of Public Health. This authority would oversee the service to assure safety and quality of service. We're not suggesting a top-heavy or expensive structure, to be sure; but some kind of responsible oversight.

Lack of follow-through – e.g., individual care-givers don't show up, or the group just stops providing the service. The same responsible authority could make sure this doesn't happen. In addition, care-givers could check in and check out via an electronic call system, or simply a cell phone or land line. The group, the patient, and maybe even some outside funding source could work together to pay for a decent monitoring system. If Neilsen can monitor TV viewing around the country, we can monitor care-giving.

Incompetent or careless care - with not only ethical but also liability implications for the care-givers and their organization. Some states' Good Samaritan laws may protect care-givers against errors and omissions of this sort, and when the service is entirely uncompensated, some homeowner's insurance policies may provide coverage.

In the meantime, the organization or a pool of similar organizations, the patient or a group of patients, an outside benefactor, or even the government itself could purchase or provide liability insurance. In addition, Affinity Groups should probably incorporate especially for liability purposes.

> *The core strength of Affinity Groups is that patients and care-givers come from the same community of values.*

Ideological abuse. It is the nature of groups that they seem driven to persuade other people to accept their values and beliefs. Some groups are extremely pushy about their beliefs, a bad mix with a vulnerable patient. A core strength of the Affinity Group program is that patients and care-givers come from the same community of values. Pre-screening of patients and care-givers would help assure a match.

Why Should This Work?

Affinity Group care-givers are more like family than typical home health aides. Research indicates that care-givers related to the patient continue to give care 50% longer than non-related care-givers. Affinity Group worker motives are more altruistic too. Those factors – sense of family and altruism – should combine to keep Affinity Group care-givers on the job, perhaps even longer than family members because they don't have the complex history with the patient that family members often have. Affinity Group care-givers will also benefit from the energy of their leader and the esprit-de-corps of the other care-givers.[4]

What Needs to Be Done?

People interested in forming an LTC Affinity Group need to do several things before they can actually start providing care. Some of the preparatory work is hard, most of it easy.

First, the hard stuff. The legal and regulatory barriers need to be removed, or some substitute protection arranged (incorporation and/or liability insurance). Care-givers should at least ask if their homeowner's insurance might cover part-time non-compensated service of this sort.

In particular, states need to exempt Affinity Groups from paralyzing licensing and reporting requirements so they can operate like informal individual caregivers, not organizations, and provide protection against legal claims when there's no malfeasance involved.

Now the easy stuff. It would help to have a national, regional, or local resource – a "clearinghouse" – that could provide information and training materials to help Affinity Groups get started and expand. The clearinghouse could also provide visibility, which in turn could attract outside funding.

A central resource could also coordinate a few experimental groups, probably starting with well established religious organizations.

It could also sponsor occasional conferences at which members of the operating groups could share their experiences.

It would be wonderful if a foundation or established organization for Seniors would "adopt" this program, at least to help it get up and running.

However, to preserve the voluntary and informal personality of the Affinity Groups, there should be a minimum of overhead.

Affinity Groups and Rationing

Rationing, as we've said, means providing less of something valuable than a person wants or needs. While Affinity Groups could not provide replacement medications or medical treatments, they could certainly provide compassion and practical lifestyle help that might make it easier for the patient to tolerate rationing. Their contribution would be compassionate care to bridge the gap between curative treatment and palliative care. On a daily basis, the match between the patient's and the group's values could enhance the care the members provide – socialization, stimulation, religious expression, and so forth. That match could even make routine care feel like a family matter and provide critical emotional support when the patient or her family are facing important healthcare decisions.

The intimate relationship between the patient and her Affinity Group could help her through even the most difficult moments.

Affinity Groups and Eschatology

The intimate relationship between the patient and her Affinity Group means that group members could help the patient through even her most difficult moments. For growing numbers of people, the most difficult moments have to do with preserving life versus hastening death.

The tension centers in values and beliefs, which means that the patient and the members of her Affinity Group are likely to be in synch about life-and-death issues. So the group is likely to respect and cooperate with the patient's decision, and help her implement it.

When it comes to preparing for the patient's final days, members of the Affinity Group could be available to support the patient's decision to persevere until the natural end, or to seek a hastened departure. The Affinity Group would certainly not try to persuade the patient in one direction or another, only support the patient's decision and try to prevent interference.

Some Affinity Groups will stay with their patients until the very end. If the very end involves any form of hastening, the blunt fact is that laws that prohibit suicide or assisted suicide will need to be honored, until they are repealed, or exceptions provided.

To summarize, we suggest that volunteer "Adopt-a-Senior" services provided by altruistic organizations, religious or secular, could help make the last years of our frail elderly not just tolerable but even vital. By providing services that elderly patients are not likely to receive otherwise, Affinity Groups could not only hold long-term care costs down but also improve the quality of that care.

Chapter 15

Individual Choices

In this chapter we're going to describe the approaches different people might take to their own long-term care. Your job is to evaluate and discuss each person's decision, with the help of the brief commentary we provide after each story.

For the sake of realism, let's say these events are going to take place sometime in the near future, after Congress and the state legislatures have had the chance to make some changes in the American long-term healthcare system. Most important, at least a few additional states have implemented QALY-based Empirical Rationing programs.

The People

Jeremiah

Jeremiah's Story. Jeremiah believed with all his heart and soul that there's nothing more sacred than Life. He viewed it as a little piece of God that it was his job to nurture until God Himself called it home.

Despite that serious side, he was a fun guy. A life insurance salesman by trade, he was gregarious, enthusiastic, and optimistic. As a kid he was active in his school's drama department, and loved being on stage. As an adult, he was active in no end of organizations. Now, in retirement, he was just as lively, although he didn't have quite the energy he had in his prime.

All his social inclinations helped him become one of his company's very best salesmen. His commissions and renewals gave him plenty of cash with which to live the good life. Before his wife died, the two of them enjoyed a company-paid perquisite trip every year – Paris, Hong Kong, Tahiti, everywhere the Beautiful People went. Despite his considerable spending, Jeremiah still managed to set aside nearly $750,000 for retirement, a third in insurance cash value, two-thirds in mutual funds. Plus there were the house and furnishings, the cars, and the time-share in Key West. Not bad for a guy who had dropped out of college during his junior year.

Jeremiah's love of life governed his attitudes toward death. He feared death as much as he valued life. He saw life as freedom, death as the ultimate loss of freedom.

So no one was surprised at what he told his doctor and the kids: "Don't let Death win – Keep me alive as long as you can." He even considered cryogenics but after kicking the idea around for the better part of a year, decided against it. It didn't really fit his view of Life.

Like many Seniors, he wanted to stay in his house as long as possible. He'd far rather die there than in some hospital or nursing home.

So he built a nice little apartment in his basement, which he planned to offer free or for a pittance to anybody who'd commit to taking care of him as his need for care grew. He was hoping for a teacher, nurse, or social worker, or maybe a student in any of those fields.

Next, he set up a trust account that kicked off enough income every month to handle his housing expenses as well as a salary for his aide. The trust principal he wanted to preserve for his daughters. He put pretty much all of his mutual fund holdings into this trust, a half million dollars.

Early on, he prepared a medical power of attorney that made it clear he wanted to stay alive under just about any circumstance he could imagine, even advanced dementia and serious pain. He figured modern palliative medicine could make his last days tolerable. His mantra was, "I'm deadly serious about Life!"

A series of strokes finally forced him out of his house. His condition was serious enough, and the doctor's prognoses adverse enough, that he by-passed the board-and-care home and went straight into a nursing home. The trust started making the $8,000 a month payments to the home, taking a big bite out of the principal each month.

His last years were more filled with tedium than pain. His mind was still pretty good, but his body was largely useless. The toughest thing for such a gregarious guy was that he could hardly speak. He felt like he was in a prison inside his own body. Many times, in his weaker moments, he wished for death. Many times he prayed for pneumonia, "the old man's friend."

Tedium became far less important when his doctors discovered colon cancer, metastasized into his liver. They gave him two years, three at the outside. Because the cancer was so far advanced and he was pretty old, the treatment didn't meet his state's QALY rationing criterion, 5%, 5 years, that is, that at least five percent of the people who received treatment would live decently for another five years. So, the most the doctors could offer him was palliative care.

Before this bombshell diagnosis, Jeremiah had thought it was nice that the good ladies of his Affinity Group would stop by now and then, to see if he needed anything, and just keep him company. They helped keep the tedium at bay. But when the chips were down – when the diagnosis was in – it was the members of the Affinity Group that made all the difference.

Morning and evening there was somebody there, making sure he was comfortable, keeping an eye on the staff, running interference with Medicare and the home's accountants, and just sitting with him. To Jeremiah, the most important thing was that, even with his limited speech, the Affinity Group members understood his commitment to Life, and supported him as he put that commitment into practice.

Late one night, near the end of his third year in the home and his third week in hospice, Jeremiah passed away. His plan had worked. While his efforts to be a good steward of his life were costly – a few hundred thousand dollars, all told – things had gone, in death as in life, pretty much the way he wanted them to.

Commentary. Think for a moment: Jeremiah was a really lucky guy. If he hadn't been as wealthy as he was, he could easily have died in a nondescript nursing home over on the other side of the tracks. And if it hadn't been for the good ladies of the St. John's Affinity Group, he could have spent his last years mostly alone and in the slough of despond.

> *The members of the Affinity Group made all the difference.*

This is the main criticism that many people – e.g., some of our friends above the northern border – have against the current American healthcare system: It's not the same for everybody. *Should* it be the same for everybody? *Could* it be the same for everybody? The only avenues to equality are to tax or to ration… or both. What's the right thing to do?

Debra

Debra's Story. Debra was a planner. She insisted on "a place for everything and everything in its place." She was as introverted as Jeremiah was gregarious, as hard-edged as he was warm and friendly. Not a lot of people wanted to spend time with her, and that was just fine as far as she was concerned. She was content with her apartment, her music, and her cats.

Debra worked in the accounting department of a Fortune 100 company. She had passed her CPA exams but decided not to practice – too risky, she felt. She'd rather have somebody telling her what to do.

Divorced for many years, Debra's sole financial goals were to have enough money to stay comfortable until she died, and to leave a little something for her three sons, even though she didn't see all that much of them since they moved away.

One of her greatest fears was that some awful debilitating disease would force her into a nursing home and eat up the little fortune she had been able to accumulate. Both her parents were in a home already, Mom with Alzheimer's, Dad with Parkinson's. She figured their ill health was a bad omen for her.

Cautious to the core, she decided to look into long-term care insurance. She just couldn't decide what to do. The more she thought about it, the more uncertain she became. On the one hand, she liked the premise of long-term care insurance – protect your assets for your heirs. If worse came to worst, she wouldn't have minded nursing-home costs eating up all her assets – except that she was adamant about leaving something for the boys.

> *One of her greatest fears was that some awful disease would force her into a nursing home and eat up what little fortune she had been able to accumulate.*

On the other hand, she thought the premium was awfully high for what she'd get. The policy she was looking at paid $150/day for five years (after a three month waiting period) and cost about $175 a month. For this amount, she would get a policy that would pay out maximum benefits of $273,750.

"Let's see. $175 a month is $2,100 a year. I'm 59, and Mom went into the home at 80. If I follow in her footsteps, I'd pay $2,100 a year for 21 years, or just over $44,000. That's a lot of money wasted if I don't go into a nursing home, or never need home- or community-based care.

"But, at $8,000 a month in the home, $44,000 is only five-and-a-half months' charges. If I live in a home for, say, five years, the insurance company would pay about $4,500 a month or $54,000 a year, for five years. That's $270,000 in benefits for $44,000 in premiums. As an investment, that sure beats my mutual funds![1]

"But I'd still have to come up with the balance, maybe $3,000 a month. I guess my Social Security would handle most of that. I might have to come up with $500-1,000 a month. Since I wouldn't have any other expenses, I should be able to do that.

"If I lived in the nursing home for more than the five years the policy would cover, I'd have to start paying $8,000 a month again, till the money ran out and I qualified for Medicaid – if it's still around and still pays for nursing homes. If I live long enough, I'd have paid all that premium and still lost everything!

"This is not a pretty picture."

Then her insurance agent made a suggestion. "There's about one chance out of four that you'll wind up in a nursing home, maybe two out of four, since your parents both went in with debilitating diseases. But there are four chances out of four that you'll die eventually. If your goal is to leave something of value to your boys, why don't you gift the premium to them and have them own a cash-value life insurance policy instead. If you pay a little higher premium up front, you'll be able to stop paying by the time you're likely to go into a home. Moreover, no matter what happens in the future, whether or not you ever need nursing-home care, your sons will receive the life insurance proceeds when you die. Bottom line: The boys will be sure to get their inheritance."

Her agent explained that a $300,000 whole life insurance policy would cost about $319 month. This would increase her monthly outlay by about $145 per month, but each son would get a nice, round $100,000. Alternatively, she and the boys could settle on smaller policy, to protect her cash flow.

Bingo! Debra signed up for the life insurance.

Twenty years later she followed in her mother's footsteps. She entered a nursing home at 80 and lived till she was 93. As a result, her life savings were consumed by her costs of care, and she went onto Medicaid. When she died, her sons, as owners and beneficiaries of the life insurance policy, divided $300,000… just in time for them to start thinking about long-term care insurance for themselves.

Commentary. The idea behind insurance is that everybody suffers a small, sure loss (the premium) so that nobody suffers a catastrophic loss (e.g., paralyzing nursing-home costs). It looks like, for future generations, some form of long-term care insurance (or life insurance) is going to be the answer to at least some of our nursing home problem.

Just like health insurance needs to be universal so people stop using emergency rooms for routine health problems, long-term care insurance needs to be universal so the only people who buy it aren't like Debra, more likely than average to end up in a home. That's what insurance people call "adverse selection," and it's what could destroy any long-term insurance program. That's part of the reason why companies are marketing so aggressively to younger people and to employer groups, so the premiums paid by the young can offset the benefits paid to the old.

If everybody had to buy long-term care insurance through their payroll taxes, the premiums might go down and the benefits might go up. Surely the benefits should be tilted toward keeping people at home, or maybe in an assisted-living center. Skilled nursing facilities ought to be a last resort.

If Debra had bought the long-term care policy she was considering, she'd have outlived her five-year benefit period. We recognize that, statistically speaking, almost half the people who enter nursing homes after age 65 die within three to five years. But that also means that almost half the people (like Debra) will live longer than five years. People who don't have clear indications that their life span will be limited ought to purchase not three- or five-year benefits, but lifetime benefits, if such a policy is available and affordable. Otherwise they might experience the worst of both worlds, paying all that premium and still out-living their benefits.

Marcus

Marcus' Story. Marcus was a businessman. If you wanted to stay on his good side, you'd better avoid all the palsy-walsy chit-chat that salesmen like to throw at prospects. Invariably he'd cut them off mid-sentence: "What's it going to do for me, and what's it going to cost – That's all I want to hear!"

There wasn't a thing about long-term healthcare that Marcus liked. First, he didn't like getting older – It made him feel vulnerable, a condition he had never been able to tolerate. He didn't like the idea of slowing down at work, to say nothing of handing over the reins. He hated the thought of losing his physical competencies – the notion of needing someone to help him to the bathroom made him physically ill. And he loathed and despised the thought of losing his mental faculties. "Shoot me now," he said more than once.

Second, growing old didn't look cost/effective. He imagined losing some of his edge at work, and missing opportunities or – worse – being outsmarted. He didn't like health insurance, and he didn't like life insurance. Both, he said, were "necessary evils" in business. He didn't even want to talk about long-term care insurance or "Affinity Groups."

It's not that he wasn't a good guy. He loved his wife and daughters, and wanted to provide for them. He loved his sisters, and wanted to do something nice for them. He appreciated his church and several different charities, and wanted to leave them significant bequests. It's just that he was, well, focused on his work.

One summer afternoon Marcus found it harder than usual to focus. His left side was twitching, and he didn't seem able to control it. When the twitching was still around a week later, Marcus went to see his internist. After a few months of testing, the doctor said he had bad news: Out of a clear blue sky, Marcus had developed ALS, Lou Gehrig's Disease. His future suddenly looked bleak.

Over the next few months Marcus spent a lot of extra time at his office, and had a number of lengthy conversations with his lawyers and his accountants. He took the family on a Mediterranean cruise. A few days after they returned home, he wrote a lengthy note, drove to his favorite state park, parked alongside a shimmering lake, and put a bullet in his head.

> *The most controversial topic in our whole book is voluntary euthanasia.*

Commentary. This brings us to perhaps the most controversial topic in our whole book: Suicide, or "voluntary euthanasia." Despite cultural and religious taboos against any form of suicide, large numbers of Seniors are talking about it, and a surprising number are, with or without the help of friendly nurses and doctors, making preparations. The taboo against suicide is weakening.

People like Marcus are more concerned about the method than the effect. To put it bluntly, most people wouldn't know how to take their own lives. One young woman, bedeviled by depression, tried to shoot herself. The bullet missed all the critical parts of the brain, and to this day, twenty years later, she lies in bed, staring at the ceiling.

Proponents of people's right to take their own lives argue that, as with abortion, the problem is some people trying to impose their religious beliefs upon others. Indeed, the State probably has a stronger interest in keeping fetuses (who have no choice) alive than in keeping very old people (who have a choice) alive.

Clearly both the proponents and opponents of voluntary euthanasia make good points. It's time to put the topic on the table so it can be part of the national conversation.

Amy

Amy's Story. The youngest daughter of two alcoholics, Amy had a profound need to help people. In grade school, she clapped erasers for the nuns. In high school, she cleaned the chapel for the priests. In college and graduate school, she majored in social work, then took a job in a private non-profit counseling center trying to help – who else? – alcoholics.

She stayed in the counseling business her whole career, changing offices only when budget cuts forced her to look for other positions. She lived a simple life, seldom partying, rarely traveling, only sometimes splurging. She preferred to hang out with a few good friends, or go camping, or take a long bike ride.

She had grown up with money, so it didn't have the allure for her that it did for others of her generation. Sometimes it annoyed her that she was living as though she had taken a vow of poverty, but by and large she was happy with her work, her play, and her friends.

The problem was, her employers could barely afford health insurance and a basic retirement plan. Her retirement would have to be even plainer than her current life, assuming Social Security stayed solvent. If it didn't, she had no idea what's she'd do. She was a Boomer, and she and her friends worried about what was going to happen when all the Boomers retired.

The thing she tried not to think about was, what would her final years be like? If her health held up, she'd just as soon die in the saddle. But that was a hope, not a plan. She knew the clinic would want her to retire as soon as she was fully eligible for Social Security; they'd want to replace her with a younger and more energetic counselor, and one would who work for even less than Amy would.

If her health didn't hold up – well, that was the rub. A couple thousand a month from Social Security and a fraction of that from her retirement fund wouldn't come near paying for a nursing home, and, besides, the new regulations made it tough to get into a decent one. She simply didn't have the money to buy long-term care insurance.

What was more likely was staying in her apartment or sharing a place with a couple of friends, a low-rent version of the Golden Girls. If worse came to worse, the next and final step would probably be a board-and-care facility of some sort. That didn't fit her self-image, but it did fit her budget.

The principal irony in Amy's life is that her parents, despite their alcoholism, had never developed cirrhosis but she – a tea-totaller – did. With that diagnosis, all her daydreams about sharing a house with other Seniors vanished, and she wound up first in a hospital, then home, then in a skilled nursing facility. To make matters as bad as they could be, her diagnosis – hepatorenal syndrome – was well below the cut-off point in her state's list of healthcare priorities. If she wanted treatment, even dialysis, she'd have to pay for it herself. The most the system could do was make her comfortable as the toxins built and she approached death.

One Fourth of July, while the rest of the community was enjoying the fireworks, Amy slipped into a coma from which she never returned.

Commentary. This is the nub of rationing – Depending on the applicable priority list, some people who don't need to die yet, will die. Amy was one of them, but not the only one. In some places, women who notice breast lumps won't be able to see a doctor for months, by which time the disease may be too far advanced to stop. The same goes for prostate cancer and other life-threatening diseases. This is where rationing becomes less abstract and very, very concrete.

> *Some people who don't need to die yet, will die. But what's the choice?*

On the other hand, what's the choice? Conditions that fall below the cut-off are those – like Amy's and Jeremiah's – that are very expensive to treat and don't lead to extending quality life by at least a few years. So doesn't it make more sense to save that money for other Seniors for whom it will do more good? Or, even for young people, who have their whole lives ahead of them?[2]

Jeannine and Guy

Jeannine and Guy's Story. Everyone who knew them envied Jeannine and Guy's relationship as well as their lifestyle. They met and married in college 50 years ago but held off on children till they had both finished graduate degrees, his in industrial psychology, hers in photojournalism. Once the fifth and final child left the nest and they could see retirement on the horizon, life took an interesting turn. Always interested in different cultures and the ways people around the world chose to deal with their problems, Jeannine and Guy decided actually to become as cosmopolitan as they had always wanted to be. Guy sold his business, and Jeannine quit her job. They liquidated most of what they had, invested it very cautiously, bought a simple little house down south mainly to store their possessions, and set out on their great adventure. They'd pick a city that excited them and rent an apartment there for a year or two. Salzburg was first on their list, a favorite ever since *The Sound of Music;* then Amsterdam, then Rome, then Athens. As they worked their way around the world, they lived frugally, but not excessively so. If money got a little tight, Guy would take a job for a few months, and Jeannine would sell another magazine article or two. They never tired of their new lifestyle, and they never tired of each other. Just the contrary, as the years passed they became more and more fond of each other, and restless when they weren't together. So you can imagine the shock when, the very same month Jeannine discovered a lump, Guy found that the reason he was slowing down wasn't age – it was pancreatic cancer. From the moment of those awful discoveries, there was no doubt in Jeannine and Guy's minds what they were going to do. A year later, when the time seemed right, they flew to Zurich and enrolled in a totally legal and entirely private specialty clinic. They took a room with two adjacent beds, where they could see and talk with each other freely. After the doctor inserted the IVs, they talked a little longer, then, as the euthanizing drugs entered their bloodstreams, smiled and slid into a deep and final sleep.

Commentary. Some people will find Jeannine and Guy's story touching, others will find it repugnant. The fact of the matter is that there are couples like Jeannine and Guy and clinics like the one in Zurich to which people go in search of a sure, painless, and dignified death. In addition, there are individuals and couples – called "suicide tourists" – who, after some awful medical news, travel to a favorite part of the world and, entirely on their own, take their own lives. American attitudes on this subject are split. According to Gallup polls, about half the country thinks physician-assisted suicide is morally acceptable while a slightly smaller percentage think it's morally wrong.[3] In the U.S., only Oregon[4] has passed legislation that permits physician-assisted suicide, but advocates in other states have tried, unsuccessfully, to pass such legislation.[5] As we said earlier, we expect that physician-assisted suicide will be among the major debates of this decade.

Chapter 16

Fourth Recapitulation

What have we learned so far that would help us design a distinctly American rationing system for long-term healthcare?

From the chapter on Affinity Groups, we've learned that there's room in the system for organized altruism, indeed that altruism could help reduce costs and at the same time improve care. Churches, businesses, social and fraternal organizations, and other collections of altruistic people could create Affinity Groups to "adopt" a Senior whose personal history, interests, and values are closely aligned with their own. Members of these groups could provide a wide variety of care, including emotional support as Grandma contemplates her end-of-life options.

From Jeremiah's, Debra's, Marcus', Amy's, and Jeannine and Guy's end-of-life stories, we were reminded that there's an enormous range of people who are facing end-of-life decisions. Their choices cover the whole range of possibilities but their circumstances often limit those choices. To put it bluntly, death isn't always fair.

We also learned that there are no really effective ways for individuals, couples, and families to protect their assets against the costs of long-term healthcare, but that some kinds of insurance might help.

In addition, we can safely assume that citizens would feel more comfortable about a healthcare rationing system if they had some meaningful input into the design and implementation; if it gave them choices; and if there were an appeals system they could trust.

While, deep down, many people would prefer a heathcare system that totally reflected their own values, individual versus communal, libertarian versus communitarian, the majority are likely to accept a balance.

With these guidelines in mind, we now proceed to our "grand summary and recommendations."

Chapter 17

Grand Summary and Recommendations

From the outset we've been trying to encourage a national conversation about *long-term* healthcare. We've taken the position that, if Congress doesn't include long-term healthcare fully and transparently in its over-all healthcare plan, we won't have any healthcare plan at all. Except for Senators Kohl's efforts (supported by Senator Baucus) to support at-home and community-based services,[1] Senator Kennedy's efforts to establish a national long-term care insurance program,[2] Senators Gregg and Conrad's efforts toward responsible fiscal action, and Senator Klobuchar's efforts toward improved eldercare, we've seen precious little sign that legislators are attending to the place of long-term care in an over-all healthcare plan.

We've been trying to encourage a national conversation about long-term healthcare.

Everybody knows that Medicaid is one of the two pillars of healthcare funding for Americans over 65.

What fewer people know is that Medicaid, generally viewed as the health program for the poor, is the principal funding source for people in nursing homes. Last year Medicaid paid nursing homes almost $73 *billion* to take care of approximately 750,000 frail elderly who had used up all their own money on medical expenses.[3]

Both Medicare and Medicaid are in serious trouble. Government experts predict that Medicare will go insolvent in about 2017, and Medicaid will become an intolerable burden to taxpayers even sooner.

Curiously, healthcare reform advocates are talking about funding a new general healthcare program (in part) by shifting hundreds of billions of dollars away from Medicare and Medicaid to the new program.

If that happens, even if the authorities mount the most aggressive cost-cutting program in the history of American healthcare, the government will have no choice but to raise taxes or expand rationing.

These decisions are too important to leave to our representatives, no matter how talented and noble they may be. To devise a long-term healthcare program that satisfies the needs of the country, the American people must step forward and engage each other, and their representatives, in a serious conversation. The purpose of this book is to get such a conversation started.

Ground Rules for the Conversation

The best decisions emerge when people can freely discuss each and every idea that's placed on the table – when the "marketplace of ideas" is fully functional.[4] It will not advance the discussion if people simply refuse to talk about some ideas because those ideas offend their personal values, their politics, or their religious beliefs. It will not advance the discussion if people try to force their views on everybody else. It will not advance the discussion if people just say No to every new idea. It should be clear by

> *The government will have no choice but to raise taxes or expand rationing – or both.*

now that things can't continue as they are.

That said, let's draw together the main points from preceding chapters as a guide for our national conversation. Let's also present some specific recommendations that people can accept, reject, or modify. However controversial some of those recommendations may be, they're all important, and they all deserve our attention.

The Three Trends

In Chapters 4, 5, and 6, we argued that growing demand for long-term care, increased difficulty recruiting and retaining direct-care workers, and rapidly rising costs are moving Medicare and Medicaid toward the brink of disaster. If we don't do something to slow or even reverse these trends, there's no way these programs can survive.

Increasing Demand

Population increases through native births and immigration are combining with advances in medicine and medical technology to create a growing population of aging people who will need long-term care. Today there are 1.5 million people in America's nursing homes. The number has been fairly steady recently, but 77 million Baby Boomers are just starting to retire, and, if past patterns are any guide, about half of them – 38.5 million! – will eventually require nursing-home care. We can barely imagine the strain the Boomers will put on the system.

The average patient stays in a nursing home for about four years, but experts predict that people with Alzheimer's, Parkinson's, diabetes, and other debilitating diseases will spend five, ten, even twenty years there.

A third of new patients are Medicaid-eligible the day they enter the home; virtually all the rest become eligible within the first three years. Everybody who's eligible for Medicaid goes onto Medicaid.

There's really no good solution to the problem of increasing demand. We've only been able to come up with three possible remedies, each of which has merit but each of which will also be repugnant to many people:

Limit immigration, which has become more important than birthrate in determining the size and nature of the American population. From the moment they set foot on American soil, a million-plus immigrants a year become eligible for participation in federal and state healthcare programs, including Medicaid's nursing-home support. As we've seen, any effort to limit immigration is bound to be controversial, and for good reason. After all, our country was built on immigration. More on point, limiting immigration could cut off what looks like our most promising future supply of direct-care workers, immigrants from countries that revere the elderly (See page 39.)

Repeal the "Nanny Laws," like requiring people to wear seatbelts and motorcycle helmets and prohibiting the recreational use of hard drugs. Outrageous as it sounds, people who choose not to behave prudently are likely to die early and not become burdens on the healthcare system. We are talking only about unpopular laws designed to protect us from ourselves and that can be empirically shown to result in a drain on the long-term healthcare system.

Permit physician-assisted suicide, that is, voluntary euthanasia. Nearly all states specifically prohibit physician-assisted suicide; only Oregon explicitly permits it. But plebiscites in several states have shown that their citizens are split nearly 50:50 on the matter, and informal conversations indicate that many Seniors would like their physicians to offer painless, sure, and dignified ways to end life. We recognize the enormous potential for abuse here, as when family members urge euthanasia for their own selfish interests. Nevertheless, we're sympathetic with the voluntary euthanasia movement, and we predict that physician-assisted suicide will become a major debate during the next decade.

Paradoxically, efforts to improve the health of the nation by diet and exercise may exacerbate the long-term care population problem. Nothing guarantees that the years you gain from wholesome living will be in the prime of life. These well-intended efforts may result in people living longer in their frail years and needing care for extended periods of time. As with the Nanny Laws, does this mean that we should go back to our old misbehavior?

Medical research, too, for all its wonders, may turn out to be a two-edged sword. Cancer and heart disease alone are responsible for more than a million deaths every year. Imagine if researchers found cures for those diseases. There'd be another million new people every year waiting in line for Medicare, and a half million waiting for Medicaid to take over their nursing-home expenses. We are not suggesting that we stop cancer and cardiovascular research or that we give up on diet and exercise, certainly not; but we are warning of some unintended and very expensive consequences.[5]

It's important not to leap quickly to conclusions pro or con about these approaches to reducing the demand for healthcare services. Each has important downsides as well as ethical and legal concerns. But the demand-for-services issue is critical, and all ideas need to be on the table.

Difficulty Recruiting and Retaining Direct-Care Workers.

Unless you spend a lot of time in nursing homes, you probably don't think about the direct-care workers, the aides, orderlies, and Certified Nursing Assistants, who do much of the hands-on work. For not a lot more money than fast-food workers earn, these people feed, groom, bathe, and otherwise care for our out-of-sight parents and grandparents. Some of the work they do is nasty, some is even dangerous.

The supply of direct-care workers is dwindling just as the demand is growing, and the pressures on these workers is going to grow as the populations they serve become sicker and more dependent. The nursing home of the future will be an even harder place to work than the nursing home of today.

Retirees and immigrants may be able to pick up some of the slack – Immigrants in particular often take jobs natives don't want – but when the Boomers start needing custodial and skilled-nursing care, there won't be nearly enough direct-care workers to meet the need, even if there's money available to pay them. In addition, language and culture differences between caregivers and residents may make it difficult for immigrant workers to interact with many frail elderly.

Affinity Groups (Chapter 14) might figure importantly here. There's real potential in this country for religious, fraternal, and even social organizations to "adopt a Senior" whose values and life experiences are consistent with their own.

In the same vein, promoting the Americorps elder-care program could encourage young people to give a year of their lives to helping care for the elderly in a nursing home or home healthcare context.[6]

Soaring Costs of Care

Assisted-living and nursing-home expenses are amazingly high and continue to grow at a rapid pace – basic charges at double the Consumer Price Index, prescription drugs quadruple that. As we pointed out in Chapter 6, the average nursing-home room already costs about $6,500 a month or $78,000 a year, in some areas half that, in other areas double. The average assisted-living apartment costs $1,500-3,000 a month; the average spot in an adult day-care center, $9.91 per hour; and the average home-health aide about $18.50 per hour. Neither Medicare nor regular health insurance pay anything for long-term care. Very few people pay out of pocket, similarly few

Our fear is that our leaders will lose sight of long-term healthcare for aging Americans.

through long-term care insurance.

What these cost increases mean for nursing-home residents and their families is that their assets will be depleted sooner. What they mean for nursing homes is that many will fall into bankruptcy.[7] What they mean for providers is that physicians and allied health professionals may turn their energies away from long-term healthcare and pursue more lucrative careers.

What the increases mean for Medicare and especially Medicaid is that eligibility standards may be raised dramatically and benefits cut substantially. Indeed, Medicaid, like Social Security, may need to return to its original purpose, to provide a healthcare "safety net" for the truly poor. In particular, Medicaid's role in paying nursing home expenses may be curtailed or even eliminated. In that case, who will pay for Grandma's nursing home?

The Administration and many legislators in both major parties are pushing hard for healthcare reform. This is important, and long overdue. Our fear is that these leaders will lose sight of *long-term* healthcare for aging Americans. On those rare occasions when they mention Medicaid, it's almost always in the context of "the health program for the poor," never as the health program that pays virtually all the expenses of nearly everybody who lives in a nursing home for more than a few years.

There are no really effective solutions for rising costs other than to increase revenues (taxation) and/or reduce benefits (rationing). The usual proposals – reduce inefficiency, eliminate fraud, and cut costs wherever you can – could help but realistically won't even come near solving the problem. We'll talk more about cost containment later in this chapter.

Who Gets Hurt by Rising Long-Term Healthcare Costs?

Before looking at the causes of soaring healthcare costs, let's review the effects we listed in Chapter 7 – Who gets hurt? The most poignant effects are those that affect the frail, elderly patients:

Anxiety. Many Seniors worry about becoming burdens on their families. Some dwell on their bleak financial futures.

Loss. The disappearance of money and property exacerbates the loss many elderly patients are already feeling.

Elder Abuse. As financial pressures increase on the whole family, more sons, daughters, and grandchildren are losing control and taking out their frustrations on the elderly through emotional abuse, physical abuse, and financial abuse.

Depression and Suicide. When depression becomes intense or sustained enough, many Seniors will seek ways to end their lives, and some will succeed. Already white males over age 65 are the most likely group to take their own lives.

There are also serious effects on these patients' families:

Increased Workload. Daughters, granddaughters, and daughters-in-law in particular are doing double-duty, taking care of their elderly relatives as well as their own families.

Doing Without. Money that would otherwise go to family needs and wants is instead going to the nursing home or assisted-care center.

Cancelled Bequests and Gifts. Most parents want to leave a bequest for their children, and perhaps a gift to a church or favorite charity. When the money is all going to healthcare, these gifts disappear. The loss is not just the money and property but what the money and property symbolize – affection, reward, etc.

Adopting a "Poverty Mentality." Many poor people see and experience the world more negatively than rich people do. Rich people who become poor see and experience it even more negatively. Advanced old age is a particularly difficult time to force people to adopt a more negative outlook on life.

There are also consequences for the people who operate and work in long-term care facilities, as well as for other patients and their families.

What's Making Long-Term Healthcare Cost So Much?

Now, what leads to these awful effects? Table 16-1 repeats the elements we listed in Chapter 8. It's easy to list them; far harder to know what to do about them. Later in this chapter we'll make some specific recommendations.

Table 16-1: Factors that Contribute to Soaring LTC Costs

Patients with Multiple Diagnoses	Drug and Related Mark-Ups
Advances in Technology	Physician Compensation
Liability Insurance for Physicians and Facilities	Excessive Entrepreneurship
Meeting Government Regulations	Over-Use by Physicians
Over-Use by Patients	Defensive Medicine
Competition for Patients	Cuts in Outside Funding
End-of-Life Treatment Costs	Failure to Monitor Costs
Inefficiency	Fraud
Insurance Company Administration	Failure to Practice Evidence-Based Medicine

The Fundamental Question

To deal with the increasing demand for services, the growing difficulty of recruiting and retaining direct-care workers, and the soaring costs of long-term healthcare, the fundamental choice is, *To Tax or To Ration.*

No surprise, the answer will almost certainly be *both* – To Tax *and* To Ration. Otherwise we won't be able to fulfill the heathcare promises we've already made, to say nothing of the breathtaking Boomer demands that are right around the corner. Bear in mind that it's by 2017 that Medicare will be insolvent,[8] and by 2027 that Congress is supposed to start re-paying the money it's borrowed from the Medicare trust fund. Nobody has any idea where that money will come from. *The Economist* recently estimated that we'd have to double the income tax just to keep Medicaid afloat.[9]

Taxation

Nobody likes taxes, and nobody likes rationing – We certainly don't! We simply don't see any alternative.

Rather than argue about *which* route to take – To Tax or To Ration – we'd like to guide the conversation toward *what kinds of (and how much) taxation* and *what kinds of (and how much) rationing* would be most palatable to the greatest number of Americans.

Tax Whom? As the push for healthcare reform got under way, the first thought was to tax rich people. According to the IRS and the Tax Foundation, the top 1% of taxpayers paid $444.4 billion in 2007, or 40.4% of the total individual taxes paid. If the goal is to raise the whole $333.2 billion (federal and state shares of Medicaid funding) by taxing the rich on their federal returns, taxes on the top 1% – adjusted gross incomes of $451,000 or more – will need to increase by 75% just to cover Medicaid (another $333 billion on top of the $444 billion), forgetting about the recent bailouts and the unfunded liabilities of Medicare and Social Security. To cast the net more broadly, the top 25% of taxpayers paid $755.7 billion. To fund Medicaid by taxing the top 25% – people with adjusted gross incomes of $66,532 or more – would require increasing their taxes by about 50%.

American taxpayers are certainly not going to tolerate increases anywhere near these.

The next thought was to tax employers. Make them either pay for healthcare for their employees or pay a penalty. But if you raise taxes on small employers, especially during a recession, they'll have less money in their compensation budgets and will either have to reduce wages or lay people off. That would be too great a price to pay to get everybody into the new healthcare program.

How about taxing healthcare *benefits*, so the health insurance coverage you get at work would be treated as additional cash income? Maybe even treat the payments you receive from your health insurer as additional income? Very negative reaction, especially from the unions.

Or maybe just tax the healthcare benefits rich people get, the so-called "Cadillac plans." Reaction seems to depend on what kind of car you drive.

Or a special tax – "Pigovian tax" – to raise revenue and discourage negative social effects, e.g., an energy tax to discourage wasting gasoline, a sugary foods tax to discourage obesity. Adam Smith himself thought this kind of tax was a good idea.[10]

Or an addition to the OASDI[11] part of your FICA (payroll) tax – To Old Age, Survivor, and Disability Income add Long-Term Care.

Or even a VAT, Value-Added Tax, a national sales tax beloved by many economists but held in low regard by many citizens who fear opening the door to yet another kind of tax.

Beyond those, what tax alternatives are there? Increased revenues will have to come from income taxes ("progressive"), payroll taxes (regressive), or some new healthcare tax or fee.

Alternatively, Congress could shift the burden at least partially to the states, which in turn would have to look at raising their income taxes or sales taxes, or charging special fees. Or the states could (indirectly) shift the burden to the counties and cities, which would have to think about increasing property taxes or maybe a special sales tax on health insurance premiums or insurance proceeds.

It never stops.

> *National sale tax (VAT) is beloved by economists but held in low regard by citizens who fear creating yet another kind of tax.*

The biggest problem with these different tax proposals is that none of them talk about how to fund *long-term* healthcare – the $78 billion that Medicaid is paying to nursing homes today, and the multiples of $78 billion that the program will be asked to pay in the future.

So, what do you think? What's the best kind of tax to increase in order to keep Medicare and Medicaid solvent, and to help Seniors around the country avoid bankruptcy?

How Much? How much tax increase do you think the American people would be willing to tolerate for long-term care purposes? How much would *you* be willing to accept? *The Economist* spoke of doubling the income tax, a 100% increase. Not happy with that – how about 75%, or 50%, or 25%, or even 10%?

This is a job for health economists, to titrate tax increases against healthcare priorities, to see where varying tax rates move the cut-off point.

While they're doing that, what's your view? At what point would a tax increase stop being a mere irritant and become a threat to your way of life?

Remember, it's a zero-sum game: The more you raise

taxes the less you'll have to expand rationing. The more you limit rationing, the more you'll have to raise taxes.

Rationing

The Concept. Rationing has a terrible reputation. We hear stories from Canada and especially England about women with breast cancer and men with prostate cancer, all denied care because the treatment or medication wasn't cost/effective. That is, the treatment wasn't likely to lead to at least a few additional years of quality life.

The question is, What might a distinctly American rationing plan look like?

Many Americans recoil at the thought of putting a dollar value on life, or at any attempt to define what is a "quality" life. Others don't like the idea of spending large amounts of money on people who are likely to die soon anyway.

To make matters worse, rationing is a cousin of "eugenics," the effort to produce a healthier society by directing care away from the frail and feeble toward those most likely to live long, vigorous, and productive lives. "Eugenics" conjures up in American minds horrible visions of Nazi exterminators herding millions of Jews, Catholics, Gays, and people with disabilities into the gas chambers of the Third Reich.

It's hard to imagine a worse reputation.

Discernment. We need to train our ears. We need to listen, but listen critically, to the TV specials and radio ads that cherry-pick the most frightening rationing stories from Canada and England, or that extol the virtues of House and Senate bills but neglect to mention the threat these bills carry for Seniors. And we need to listen equally closely to the proposals that talk about shifting billions of dollars from Medicare and Medicaid to a new healthcare program. Those proposals are code for, Let's ration Senior healthcare so we have enough money to insure the people in this country who aren't already insured. Whom shall we favor – the old, or the uninsured?

The airways are full of euphemism, distortion, and even deceit.

The fact of the matter is that, while no form of rationing is attractive, not all rationing is the same. The question is, What might a distinctly American rationing plan look like? Is it possible to develop a rationing plan that Americans will accept?

Let's explore this new territory.

Toward a Distinctly American Long-Term Healthcare Rationing Plan

Long-term healthcare rationing has got to be viewed in the context of over-all healthcare rationing. Right off the bat that means that we have to ask if our rationing plan should favor the young, the middle-aged, or the old.

Favor the Young? The Young have their whole lives ahead of them. It's they upon whom the future of the country depends. To achieve the greatest benefit for the country, doesn't it make sense that our healthcare rationing system should favor the Young?

Keep in mind that the Young most vulnerable to rationing are newborns and infants with birth defects, and those who have contracted, surely through no fault of their own, horrible diseases and suffered awful deformities, many congenital. These are terribly sad cases, and also very expensive.

Favor the Middle-Aged? The Middle-Aged are the people who are making the country work, the ones who are creating jobs, expanding businesses, and doing the yeoman's labor of holding everything together. They're simultaneously paving the way for the Young and easing the burdens of the Old. Doesn't it make sense that our healthcare rationing system should favor the Middle-Aged?

The most vulnerable middle-aged people are those who have been grievously injured – brain damage comes to mind, but also other incapacitating physical injuries and cognitive and emotional trauma, perhaps from accidents or assault, perhaps because the victims were doing foolish or even illegal things. Can people so seriously injured be returned to a productive life? At what cost, paid by whom?

Favor the Old? The Old are enjoying the fruits of their lifetime of labor, what we (often tongue-in-cheek) call their "Golden Years." They are the repositories of wisdom and experience who can – if listened to, as in other cultures – smooth the way for the generations that follow them. Doesn't it make sense that our healthcare rationing system should favor the Old?

The elderly people most vulnerable to rationing are those whose bodies or minds have given out sooner than other people's – surely those with the major debilitating diseases like Alzheimer's, Parkinson's, and ALS, but also the very, very old who are suffering any of a myriad of life-threatening diseases including but not limited to cancer, tuberculosis, and diabetes. These too are sad cases, but cases for which extensive medical care is dubiously cost/effective.

Most healthcare philosophers propose favoring the Young.[12] It's a difficult position to challenge, but it suffers what we consider a fatal flaw: It dismisses the vital elderly, those septua-, octo-, and nonagenarians who are physically fit and cognitively effective. Our alternative is to favor the Healthy, those who, regardless of age, have the best chance to recover from their illness or injury and live a happy and productive life.

What do *you* think? In an environment in which we just can't provide all the care we'd like to, whose healthcare shall we limit, and whose shall we favor?

Empirical Versus Clinical Rationing

Of what might an American rationing plan consist? In Chapters 10 and 11 we described two principal kinds of rationing: Empirical Rationing and Clinical Rationing. Rationing experts would list many variations on these themes.

Empirical Rationing

At the core of Empirical Rationing is a list of illnesses and treatments ranked from the most to the least cost/effective. Those treatments the system can afford, it will pay for; those it can't afford, it won't. The general idea is that a treatment must be likely to result in at least a few more years of decent-quality life for a significant percentage of the people who receive it. If it doesn't meet those criteria, you can have it but you must pay for it on your own. Owing to the cost of many procedures, if the program won't fund it, most patients won't receive it.

If you want to cover a wider range of illnesses, you add more money to the system; if you want to save money, you restrict the budget. Ultimately the decisions rest not with those who rank the illnesses and treatments but with those who control the purse.

Study the priority list in Appendix A. If Oregon wanted to cover more illnesses, the governor and legislature could add money to the system and lower the cut-off point. If the authorities wanted to save money in a lean year, they could raise the cut-off point.

Does the Oregon plan seem reasonable? Are there treatments below the cut-off line you would require the state to pay for? Any above the cut-off that you think people should have to pay for themselves?

The Oregon plan, the Canadian plan, and the English plan are conceptually similar. They're all instances of Empirical Rationing. They differ in where they set their cut-off point, and whether they permit people to purchase supplementary insurance to cover what the government programs don't.

Often *but not always* Empirical Rationing includes the opportunity to buy private insurance to protect against maladies the rationing system doesn't pay for. Countries that prohibit supplementary insurance are focused on egalitarianism, a level, horizontal playing field for everybody. Those that permit supplementary insurance are more inclined to honor human variation, a vertical or hierarchical view of the world.

Offering this kind of insurance presents real "adverse selection" problems for insurance companies, but it also helps citizens feel they have some control over their lives.

We suspect that, if an American system prohibited supplementary insurance there would immediately develop a healthcare Black Market, and thousands more people than now would be flying to Bangkok, Singapore, Bangalore and other Asian cities for treatment.

Clinical Rationing

Clinical Rationing, in contrast, has been widespread in America for years, perhaps decades. Clinical Rationing occurs when your doctor decides what treatment, or absence of treatment, is reasonable in the light of your physical and emotional history, current status, and prognosis. It puts the responsibility on your physician, who presumably knows you better, to make a situational judgment about what treatment or medication is best under the circumstances -- curative or palliative, name-brand or generic. Most Americans seem to prefer Clinical Rationing over Empirical Rationing (p. 90, above), especially when Clinical Rationing is informed by empirically derived healthcare priority lists.

As American medicine moves inexorably toward some state or national version of an obligatory HMO, doctors will be increasingly beholden to their employers. Mandated to follow the employer's priority rules and compensated in terms of cost/effectiveness – capitation – they will lose some independence, and Clinical Rationing will begin to approximate Empirical Rationing. In time the two approaches – Empirical and Clinical – may very well become one and the same.

Ethics and Rationing

The decision to tax or to ration isn't just about saving money versus withholding care. It's about *What's the right thing to do?* So, in Chapter 10, we provided a brief overview of the ethics of rationing.

Because what's one person's right is another person's wrong, we applied widely accepted principles of ethics to key rationing questions. From the myriad available, we selected three especially well known principles:

> The Golden Rule: *Do unto others as you would have others do unto you.*
>
> The Utilitarian Principle: *Seek the greatest happiness for the greatest number.*
>
> The Categorical Imperative: *Behave in such a way that what you do could become a universal moral law.*

We applied these principles to three illustrative questions about rationing:

> *Is it the right thing to do,* to deprive some people of needed healthcare in order to keep other people's taxes affordable?
>
> *Is it the right thing to do,* to deprive people of medicine and medical treatments if their illness is the result of their own bad behavior, e.g., smoking?
>
> *Is it the right thing to do,* to participate in euthanasia?

Suffice it to say that there will be plenty of debate about what goes above the line and what goes below it, and where exactly that line should be

We found more consistency than we expected between what these ethical principles prescribed and the Empirical Rationing priorities of the Oregon system. The key seems to be to keep as many life-saving procedures as possible above the cut-off line, lesser procedures below. In years of fat, there may be no life-saving procedures excluded from the program; in years of lean, there will almost surely be some. Similarly, in fat years the threshold for a permissible procedure could be lowered. The five year, five percent criterion – already quite low - could be softened to five years, two percent, that is, five additional years of quality life for at least two percent of the cases. In lean years, the threshold could be toughened, e.g., likely to produce five more good years of life for ten percent of the population, or more.

Suffice it to say that there will be plenty of room for vigorous debate about what goes above, and what goes below, the cut-off, and how high that cut-off should be.

Practice

So you could get a "feel" for what it would be like to design and implement a rationing system or sit on a local rationing board, we provided lots of practice opportunity.

In Chapter 11, we presented fifteen case studies in which you encountered some of the conflicts and temptations people charged with rationing must deal with. In Chapter 15, we presented another five case studies so you could see, close up, the decisions Seniors need to make and the consequences of those decisions. Throughout the book we presented personal stories – e.g., Emily's Story – that give you a glimpse into people's lives and daily health-care struggles. In addition to being instructive, we hope these stories have "humanized" the book.

Among the things we learned from the case studies were:

You'll be tempted to let your emotions override your intellect, as when one patient is likeable and the other is a jerk.

You might be tempted to use factors you shouldn't, like sex and race, even religion.

You might be tempted to apply your own brand of justice, as when somebody who got away with a heinous crime may also seem to be getting a break with rationing.

You may need to bite your tongue when it sometimes seems like you have to make a decision that's unjust.

You may sometimes have to "pull the plug" on a vulnerable person because her prognosis doesn't justify spending what the prescribed treatment would cost.

You may even have to say no to someone who desperately needs a particular treatment, just because she's too old or too infirm to justify the cost.

Prescriptions

Our goal is not to fix all the problems all at once. Too many Seniors would be thrown into chaos with no time to prepare for the changes, and the changes in general would be too complex to handle all at once. Rather, targeting the experts' recommendations (p. 79, above), we aim first to slow, then stop, the rise in long-term healthcare costs, then gradually to reduce it. The difference lies in how many, and which, prescriptions one applies, and when.

To that end, we began with a proposal that we return to some of the ways of our ancestors. We believe that there are altruistic people around the country who would welcome an opportunity to work with the frail elderly. This is not simply a volunteer care-giver proposal. Key to this proposal is an intimate "affinity" between patient and care-giver, a connection in life's most important values. Affinity Groups will often be religious but there's no reason they can't be connected with fraternal, corporate, social or other kinds of organizations. Affinity Groups will offer more than assistance with the activities of daily life. They will offer the opportunity to talk about even the most sensitive topics that concern people in their later

> *The key to a successful Affinity Group is a connection in life's most important values.*

years. Topics would include family issues, personal matters, religious concerns, even end-of-life decisions. We talk in greater detail in Chapter 14.

Now we move to a variety of financial efforts to contain cost, after that on to what we believe is a "distinctly American rationing system."

A distinctly American rationing plan would be characterized by choice, citizen input, sensitivity to individual circumstances, an appeals process, and a balance of individual and community values.

General Cost Control

Effect Tort Reform – Tighten the definition of malpractice or the caps on malpractice awards, so doctors don't have to waste so much money practicing defensive medicine. Provide appeals juries so truly abusive malpractice doesn't fall through the cracks.

Revise Physician Compensation – Find ways to reward quality more than quantity; and to improve compensation for primary-care and geriatric physicians.

Control the Advance of Technology – Limit government funding to technological research that is likely to produce cost/effective products. Direct some technological research funding toward training more primary-care and geriatric physicians, physician's assistants, and nurse practitioners;

Monitor Practice Costs – Adopt the attitude and evidence- and data-based procedures of institutions like the Mayo Clinic and the Cleveland Clinic.

Review Physician Entrepreneurship – Try to reverse the culture that has made medicine in some quarters excessively profit-centered.

Contain Patients' Moral Hazard – Especially if universal coverage becomes a reality, take steps to help patients understand the real costs of the treatments and medications they demand, and require them to pay a greater share of those costs (e.g., higher co-payments).

Encourage At-Home Care – Promote programs designed to help frail elderly who can possibly continue to live at home to do so, e.g. adult day-care centers.

Constrain Fraud and Inefficiency – Explore whatever methods become available for identifying and reducing fraud against the healthcare system, and for identifying and correcting inefficiency.

Promote Information Technology – Streamline record-keeping (and battle fraud and inefficiency) through computer technology, at the same time maintain strict safeguards for individual privacy.

Rationing Plan

So, what would a "distinctly American" rationing plan look like? It would be characterized by choice, citizen input into design and operation, sensitivity to individual needs and circumstances, an appeals process, and a balance of individual and community values. More specifically:

Balance Taxation and Rationing – It would optimize the balance between taxation and rationing, so as many proven life-saving treatments as possible are above the healthcare priorities cut-off line, and that below that line sit the less critical, more infrequent, and more expensive treatments.

Balance Empirical and Clinical Rationing – For the rationing part, optimize the balance between Empirical Rationing and Clinical Rationing, leaving the ultimate decision to the patient's own doctors. Require that doctors who want to depart from their state's rationing priorities justify their request to a peer-review panel.

Publicize Empirical Rationing Priorities – With regard to Empirical Rationing, prepare and publish widely national or –

better – state-by-state healthcare priorities after the fashion of the Oregon procedure.

Use Graded Co-Payments – Instead of binary above/below-the-line decisions, scale co-payments from, say, 90% to 0% depending on the cost/effectiveness of the procedure or medication, or the health of the patient.

Establish Rationing Juries – Provide rationing juries composed of lay people as well as medical experts to hear physician and patient appeals to initial rationing decisions.

Require LTC Insurance – Require everyone to purchase long-term care insurance through payroll taxes or with their tax returns, and make sure everybody recognizes the limits of the basic coverage (Kennedy plan).

Encourage "Rati-Gap" Insurance – Encourage people to purchase private Ration-Gap insurance to cover treatments and medications below the cut-off on the state's healthcare priorities list or that would otherwise be denied them.

Promote At-Home Care – Reward families for taking care of their elderly at home, and encourage support services like home health aides and adult day-care (Kohl program), and Affinity Groups (Chapter 14).

Favor the Healthy – Favor neither the Young over the Old nor the Old over the Young. Rather, favor the Healthy – those likely to live long enough and well enough to justify the treatment or medication – over the Unhealthy.

Monitor Seniors' Health – Encourage regular medical check-ups for people over 75 so those in good health will have better access to rationed treatments and medications than those in ill health.

Define "Quality of Life" – Establish a definition for "quality of life" in the specific context of the elderly.

Promote Affinity Groups -- Encourage the formation of long-term care Affinity Groups, and reward the organizations that sponsor successful such groups. At the same time, protect the groups and their members from frivolous lawsuits.

Promote Select Medical Specialties – Give incentives to physicians who are willing to specialize in select below-the-cut areas to bring down the cost and move particularly important treatments up above the cut.

Expand Allied Professional Roles -- Expand the role of physician's assistants and nurse practitioners in long-term health care.

Encourage Primary Care and Geriatric Specialties – Open medical school doors to more students who are willing to commit to primary-care and geriatric practice, and "incent" doctors to practice in these areas.

Promote Americorps' Eldercare Program – Promote the Americorps elder-care program that lets young people earn forgiveness of student loans by working in a long-term care facility or home-healthcare context.

Revise Immigration Laws – Revise immigration laws to favor immigrants from countries that revere the elderly who would work in long-term care facilities. Create an exception rule for those who would agree to work as direct care workers in long-term healthcare for a specified period of time.

Repeal Select Nanny Laws – Reduce the demand for long-term care by repealing those "Nanny Laws" that empirical study shows are worsening the long-term care problem, e.g., those laws requiring motorcycle helmets and banning the recreational use of Class A narcotics.

Educate the Elderly about End-of-Life Planning – Educate the elderly about the importance of early end-of-life planning, and make Do-Not-Resuscitate (DNR) the "default position" for people entering long-term care facilities under government funding.

Permit Voluntary Euthanasia – Reduce the demand also by allowing voluntary euthanasia (physician-assisted suicide) and, in accessible clinics around the country, provide the means for a sure, painless, and dignified death pursuant to the patient's wishes. Devise safeguards to prevent abuse.

One of our goals in devising this proposal was to provide for as much choice as possible. The most important instances of choice are: 1) Choice about purchasing supplemental LTC insurance, which could make all the difference if the patient develops a below-the-cut condition; 2) Choice to participate in an Affinity Group program; 3) Choice to work with a physician's assistant or clinical nurse practitioner when a physician's services are not absolutely required; 4) Choice about the provisions of a living will or durable medical power of attorney; 5) Choice about having or not having a Do-Not-Resuscitate order; 6) Choice about voluntary euthanasia.

We also wanted meaningful citizen input in the design and implementation of the program. Citizen participation occurs in 1) Determining the balance between taxation and rationing; 2) Defining "quality of life"; 3) Determining the healthcare priority rankings; 4) Participating on rationing juries; 5) Forming and implementing Affinity Groups; and 6) Participating in the Americorps eldercare program.

The third criterion was sensitivity to individual needs and circumstances: 1) Emphasize Clinical Rationing; 2) Encourage the purchase of supplementary LTC insurance; 3) Repeal some Nanny State laws to allow individual choice; 4) Favor the Healthy rather than either the Young or the Old; 5) Encourage regular check-ups so healthy Seniors will continue to have access to treatment, and 6) Use graded co-payments.

The fourth was an appeals process: The rationing juries.

The fifth and final criterion for a distinctly American rationing plan was a balance of individual and community values: 1) Balancing Empirical and Clinical Rationing; 2) Require everybody to purchase basic LTC insurance from an early age; 3) Reward families for taking care of their elderly at home.

There you have it, our best shot at a long-term healthcare plan for aging Americans that at once faces the hard realities of 21st-century health economics, hopes to slow increasing healthcare costs, and contains enough safeguards that a majority of Americans might be able to accept it.

We solicit your reactions.

Endnotes

Chapter 1: What We Want to Accomplish, and Why

[1] **Medicare Payments to Nursing Homes.** Visit: http://www.aahsa.org/NationalExpenditureData/.

[2] **$38 Trillion.** Boards of Trustees, Federal Hospital Insurance and Federal Supplementary Medical Insurance Trust Funds. (2009). 2009 Annual Report.

[3] **2027.** Boards of Trustees, Federal Hospital Insurance and Federal Supplementary Medical Insurance Trust Funds. (2009). 2009 Annual Report.

[4] **Nursing Home Demographics.** Kasper, Judith, and Molly O'Malley (2007). Changes in Characteristics, Needs, and Payment for Care of Elderly Nursing Home Residents: 1999 to 2004. Kaiser Commission on Medicaid and the Uninsured. In 2009, federal and state Medicaid spending on nursing home care will total $333.2 billion. For more on young people with disabilities, see Kane (1999).

[5] **Medicaid-Eligible.** Waitmann, Timothy, and Korbin Liu. (2006). Asset Transfer and Nursing Home Use: Empirical evidence and policy significance. Kaiser Commission on Medicaid and the Uninsured. The federal share will be $190.6 billion, or 57%. The states will be responsible for the balance, $142.6 billion.

[6] **Spending on Nursing Home Care.** Visit: http://www.aahsa.org/NationalExpenditureData/. State percentages vary widely, so we expect an increase in "Medicaid shopping." See also: Department of Health and Human Services (2008). Actuarial Report.

[7] **Stop Paying for Nursing Home Care.** Barrick, Daniel. (2004). Medicaid Overhaul Outlined. Concord *Monitor,* October 20, 2004,

[8] **Filial Responsibility Laws.** See Pakula, Matthew (2005). The Legal Responsibility of Adult Children to Care for Indigent Parents. National Center for Policy Analysis, No. 521. Available at: http://www.ncpa.org/pub/ba521. For a list of the 30 states and citations to their statutes, visit: http://everydaysimplicity.blogspot.com/2006/02/filial-responsibility-laws-list-of.html.

[9] **$78,000.** Visit: www.AAHSA.org. Aging Services: The Facts.

[10] **Hundreds of Billions.** See, for example, www.whitehouse.gov/MedicareFactSheetFinal/. See also, http://www.whitehouse.gov/the_press_office/Remarks-by-the-President-to-a-Joint-Session-of-Congress-on-Health-Care/.

[11] ***The Economist.*** *The Economist,* June 13, 2009, p. 34.

Chapter 2: Medicare and Medicaid

[1] **Medicare, Medicaid.** For a primer on Medicare and Medicaid, visit http://www.medicare.gov/LongTermCare/Static/Home.asp

[2] **Obligations to the Medicare Trust Fund.** Over the years, Congress has borrowed money from the Medicare Trust Fund for various purposes, using "preferred" bonds as security. These loans are scheduled for repayment from general revenues starting in 2027. How general revenues will be able to handle these payments remains an open question. At a minimum, they will require substantial tax increases. See: 2009 Annual Report of the Board of Trustees of the Federal Hospital Insurance and Federal Supplementary Medical Insurance Trust Funds. See also Vogel, Ronald J. (1999). *Medicare: Issues in political economy.* Ann Arbor: University of Michigan Press.

[3] **Government's Program for the Poor.** The federal government matches, on a formula basis, state expenditures. As a consequence, federal contributions vary from 50-83% of actual state expenditures.

[4] **Nursing Home Stays.** Komisar, H.L., J. Feder and J.D. Kasper. (2005).

Unmet Long-Term Care Needs: An Analysis of Medicare-Medicaid Dual Eligibles. *Inquiry 42*(2): 171-182.

[5] **Medicaid-Eligible at Admission.** Kaiser Commission on Medicaid and the Uninsured. (2006). Medicaid and Long-Term Care Services

[6] **Nursing-Home Demographics.** Kasper, Judith, and Molly O'Malley (2007). Changes in Characteristics, Needs, and Payment for Care of Elderly Nursing Home Residents: 1999 to 2004. Kaiser Commission on Medicaid and the Uninsured.

[7] **New Residents Sicker.** Kasper, Judith, and Molly O'Malley. (2007). Changes in Characteristics, Needs, and Payment for Care of Elderly Nursing Home Residents: 1999 to 2004. Kaiser Commission on Medicaid and the Uninsured. http//:www.kff.org.

[8] **Patient Days.** Medicaid patients are the longest stayers. American Health Care Association. (n.d.). Nursing Home Statistics. http://www.efmoody.com/longterm/nursingstatistics.html.

Chapter 4: Trend I – Growing Demand for Long-Term Healthcare

[1] **Alzheimer's Association Predictions.** 2009 Alzheimer's Disease Facts and Figures. To be published in Alzheimer's Association, *Alzheimer's & Dementia,* Volume 5, Issue 3. Available at: http://www.alz.org/national/documents/report_alzfactsfigures2009.pdf.

[2] **Growth Rates by Race.** http://pewhispanic.org/states/population/

[3] **Census Bureau Projections.** Day J.C. (2001) National population projections. U.S. Census Bureau. On-Line at: http://www.census.gov/population/www/pop-profile/natproj.html.

[4] **Deaths from Heart Disease and Cancer.** http//:www.AmericanHeartAssociation.org. http//www.AmericanCancerSociety.org. See Stone, Robyn I. (2000). Long-term Care for the Elderly with Disabilities. Millbank Memorial Fund. http//:www.milbank.org/0008stone/.

[5] **Immigration Statistics.** Yearbook of Immigration Statistics (2008). Department of Homeland Security: http://www.dhs.gov/files/statistics/publications/yearbook.shtm. See also Mongren, Randall, and Nancy Rytina. (2009). U.S. Legal Permanent Residents: 2008. Annual Report. Department of Homeland Security.

[6] **States with Most Foreign-Borns.** . http://www.census.gov/population/www/socdemo/foreign/maps/TFB_Pntdist.pdf

[7] **Projections.** http://en.wikipedia.org/wiki/Demographics_of_the_United_States

[8] **Illegal Immigration.** Passel, Jeffrey S., and D'Vera Cohn.(2008). *Trends in Unauthorized Immigration: Undocumented inflow now trails legal inflow.* Washington, DC: Pew Hispanic Center, October 2008. On-Line: http://pewresearch.org/pubs/978/undocumented-immigration.

[9] **Minority Becomes Majority.** Aizenman, N. C. (2008). U.S. to Grow Grayer, More Diverse. Washington Post, August 14, p. A06.

[10] **Life Expectancies 1900-2005.** Visit http://www.cdc.gov/nchs/data/hus/hus08.pdf#026.

[11] **Life Expectancies by Race and Sex.** http://www.cdc.gov/nchs/data/hus/hus08.pdf#026.

[12] **People Needing Long-Term Healthcare.** U.S. Department of Health and Human Services (2003); emphasis added.

[13] **Baby Boomers Retiring.** Baby Boomers' Retirement Prospects: (2003). An Overview. Congressional Budget Office, November.

[14] **Connections with Race and Ethnicity.** Berkman, Lisa F., and Ichirō Kawachi. (2000). *Social epidemiology.* New York: Oxford University Press US.

[15] **Alzheimer's by Race.** http://www.alz.org/national/documents/report_africanamericanssilentepidemic.pdf
http://www.alz.org/national/documents/report_hispanic.pdf

[16] **Parkinson's by Race.** Stephen K. Van Den Eeden, Stephen K., Caroline M. Tanner, Allan L. Bernstein, Robin D. Fross, Amethyst Leimpeter, Daniel A. Bloch, and Lorene M. Nelson. (2003). Incidence of Parkinson's Disease: Variation by age, gender, and race/ethnicity. *American Journal of Epidemiology,* 157, 1015-22.

[17, 18, 19] **TB by Race.** http://publichealth.lacounty.gov/tb/facts/2005fact/2005Fact_Asian.pdf. See also: Cantwell, Michael F., Matthew T. McKenna, Eugene McCray, and Ida M. Onorato. (1998). Tuberculosis and Race/Ethnicity in the United States: Impact of socioeconomic status. *American Journal of Respiratory Critical Care Medicine.* 157(4), 1016-1020.

[20] **Diabetes by Race.** American Diabetes Association, http://www.diabetes.org/diabetes-statistics/prevalence.jsp

[21] **Heart Disease by Race.** http://www.americanheart.org/presenter.jhtml?identifier=4650. See also www.americanheart.org/presenter.jhtml?identifier=4726.

[22] **Multiple Conditions.** Kasper, Judith, and Molly O'Malley. (2007). Changes in Characteristics, Needs, and Payment for Care of Elderly Nursing Home Residents: 1999 to 2004. Kaiser Commission on Medicaid and the Uninsured. http//:www.kff.org.

[23] **Bankruptcy Protection.** In 2004 alone, five out of the 10 largest chains that provide long-term care filed for bankruptcy protection. 52% of all nursing homes are part of a chain. AHCA. (2004). Nursing Home Statistics.

[24] **Americans 85 and Older.** U. S. Census Bureau.

Chapter 5: Trend II – Increasing Difficulty Finding Direct Care Workers

[1] **Recruiting Staff.** Center for the Health Professions. (2006). An Aging U.S. Population and the Health Care Workforce: Factors affecting the need for geriatric care workers. University of California, San Francisco. See also: Institute for the Future of Aging Services (2007). The Long-Term Care Workforce: Can the crisis be fixed? See also: Friedlan, R. (2004). Caregivers and Long-Term Care Needs in the 21st Century: Will public policy meet the challenge? Issue Brief. Washington D.C.: Georgetown University Long-Term Care Financing Project.

[2] **Improving DCW Jobs.** Kemper, Peter, Barry T, Heier, D. Brannon, J. Angelelli, J., M. Anderson-Knott. (2008). What do Direct Care Workers Say Would Improve Their Jobs? Differences across settings. *The Gerontologist,* Special Issue 1, 17-25.

[3] **IFAS Survey.** Institute for the Future of Aging Services (2007). The Long-Term Care Workforce: Can the crisis be fixed?

[4] **Major Workforce Issue.** Austin, Bonnie G., J.D. and Lisa K. Fleisher. (2003). Financing End-of Life Care: Challenges for an aging population. Academy Health is the national program office for HCFO, an initiative of The Robert Wood Johnson Foundation. Available on line at: http://www.hcfo.net/pdf/eolcare.pdf. See also: Harmuth, S. and S..Dyson. (2004). Results of the 2003 National Survey of State Initiatives on the Long-Term Care Direct-Care Workforce. Paraprofessional Healthcare Institute; and the North Carolina Department of Health and Human Services, Office of Long Term Care, New York.

[5] **DCW Demographics.** Institute for the Future of Aging Services (2007). The Long-Term Care Workforce: Can the crisis be fixed?

[6] **Low-Income Women.** What do Direct Care Workers Say Would Improve Their Jobs? Differences across settings. *The Gerontologist, 48,* Special Issue 1 (2008).

[7] **On-the-Job Risks.** Institute for the Future of Aging Services (2007). The Long-Term Care Workforce: Can the crisis be fixed?

[8] **Turnover.** Institute for the Future of Aging Services. (2007). The Long-Term Care Workforce: Can the crisis be fixed? See also: http://blog.directcarealliance.org/category/direct-care-workers/and-turnover/

[9] **Turnover.** Institute for the Future of Aging Services (2007). The Long-Term Care Workforce: Can the crisis be fixed?

[10] **Turnover.** Institute for the Future of Aging Services (2007). The Long-Term Care Workforce: Can the crisis be fixed?

[11] **CNA Status.** (2005). "Who wants to be a CNA? *Journal of Nursing Administration,* 35(9), September, p. 380.] See also: (2005). *The Meaning of Work for Nursing Assistants Who Stay in Long-Term Care.* Blackwell Publishing, Ltd. (2005).

[12] **Emotional Well-Being.** Mutaner, C., Y. Li, X. Xue, P. O'Campo, H.J. Chung, and W.W. Eaton. (2004). Work Organization, Area Labor-Market Characteristics, and Depression among U.S. Nursing Home Workers: A cross-classified multi-level analysis. *International Journal of Occupational and Environmental Health. 10,* 392-400. See also: Noelker, L.S. and Z. Harel. (2000). *Quality of Life and Quality of Care in Long-Term Care.* New York: Springer. See also: Stone, R.I., and J. M. Weiner. (2001) *Who Will Care for Us? Addressing the long-term care worker crisis.* Washington DC: Urban Institute and American Association of Homes and Services for the Aging.

[13] **Racism.** Ejaz, Farida K., Linda S. Noelker, Heather L. Menne, and Joshua G. Bagaka. (2008). The Impact of Stress and Support on Direct Care Workers' Job Satisfaction. *The Gerontologist, 48,* Special Issue I, 60-70.

[14] **Women as Caregivers.** (2008). Retention of Paid Related Caregivers: Who Stays and Who Leaves Home Care Careers?" *The Gerontologist, 48,* Special Issue 1.

[15] **Women in the Work Force.** United States Department of Labor (2009). Quick Stats on Women Workers: 2008. Visit: http//:www.dol.gov/wb/stats/main.htm.

[16] **Limitations on Family Caregivers.** See: Stone, Robyn I. (2000). Long-term Care for the Elderly with Disabilities. Millbank Memorial Fund. http//:www.milbank.org/0008stone/. See also: American Health Care Association. (n.d.). Nursing Home Statistics. http://www.efmoody.com/longterm/nursingstatistics.html.

[17] **Older Caregivers.** (2008). Older Workers: An opportunity to expand the long-term care/direct care labor force.", *The Gerontologist, 48,* Special Issue I, 90-103.

Chapter 6: Trend III – Soaring Costs of Long-Term Healthcare

[1] **Filial Responsibility Laws.** See Pakula, Matthew (2005). The Legal Responsibility of Adult Children to Care for Indigent Parents. National Center for Policy Analysis, No. 521. Available at: http://www.ncpa.org/pub/ba521. For a list of the 30 states and citations to their statutes, visit: http://everydaysimplicity.blogspot.com/2006/02/filial-responsibility-laws-list-of.html.

[2] **Types of Long-Term Healthcare.** For overviews of types of long-term healthcare, see:
http://www.medicare.gov/LongTermCare/Static/TypesOverview.asp
http://www.mayoclinic.com/health/long-term-care/HA00054

[3] **PACE.** For details on the PACE program, visit:
http://www.medicare.gov/Nursing/Alternatives/Pace.asp

[4] **Local Programs.** For information on Meals on Wheels, visit: http://www.mowaa.org/Page.aspx?pid=183
For information on respite care, visit: http://helpguide.org/elder/respite_care.htm.
See also American Health Care Association's Home Care Finder: http://www.tlchoices.com/hcfinder/

[5] **Genworth Map.** To access Genworth's interactive map on long-term care costs throughout the U.S., visit: https://pro.genworth.com/content/products/long_term_care/long_term_care/cost_of_care.html. For general descriptions of kinds of long-term care services, visit: http://www.mayoclinic.com/health/long-term-care/HA00054

[6] **Another Genworth Report.** For summary statistics on long-term healthcare costs, visit: https://pro.genworth.com/content/etc/medialib/genworth_v2/pdf/ltc_cost_of_care.Par.73347.File.dat/Summary%20of%20Findings_gnw.pdf.

[7] **Dependent Tax Credit.** For information on the Dependent Tax Credit, visit: http://www.irs.gov/taxtopics/tc602.html.

[8] **Adult Day-Care Costs.** https://pro.genworth.com/content/etc/medialib/genworth_v2/pdf/ltc_cost_of_care.Par.73347.File.dat/Summary%20of%20Findings_gnw.pdf.

[9] **Adult Day-Care.** The National Respite Network and Resource Center provides useful information on adult day-care: http://www.archrespite.org/archfs54.htm.

[10] **Home-Care Finder.** http://www.tlchoices.com/hcfinder/

[11] **Veterans' Benefits.** Special benefit programs are available for veterans at (800) 827-1000.

[12] **Facility Finder.** http://www.tlchoices.com/finder/find-nursing-home.asp?CID=35.

[13] **Skilled Nursing Facility.** For definition and detailed description, visit: http://helpguide.org/elder/nursing_homes_skilled_nursing_facilities.htm.

[14] **Medicaid Regulations.** *TLC Choices* is constructing a website that will guide you to the Medicaid requirements for your state: http://www.tlchoices.com/experts/medicaid.asp.

[15] **Partnerships for Long-Term Care.** Attend to the "Confidence in Long-Term Care Insurance Age of 2009," recently introduced by Senator Herb Kohl's Special Committee on Aging: http://www.opencongress.org/bill/111-s1177/show. Kudos also to the Robert Wood Johnson Foundation and Genworth Financial for trying to promote this program nationally.

Chapter 7: Consequences of Rising Long-Term Care Costs

[1] **Losses.** For details, see Doyle, Kenneth O. (1999). *The Social Meanings of Money and Property: In search of a talisman.* Thousand Oaks CA: Sage.

[2] **Definitions of Elder Abuse.** Visit: http://www.ncea.aoa.gov.

[3] **Elder Abuse on the Rise.** The National Center on Elder Abuse presents this fact sheet: http://www.ncea.aoa.gov/NCEAroot/Main_Site/pdf/2-14-06%2060FACT%20SHEET.pdf.

[4] **Gifts.** It should be mentioned that, for Medicaid purposes, all gifts need to end more than five years prior to application for Medicaid benefits.

Chapter 8: Why Does Long-Term Care Cost So Much?

[1] **Multiple Conditions.** Kasper, Judith, and Molly O'Malley. (2007). Changes in Characteristics, Needs, and Payment for Care of Elderly Nursing Home Residents: 1999 to 2004. Kaiser Commission on Medicaid and the Uninsured. http//:www.kff.org.

[2] **Costly Competition.** For a rather old but technically excellent report, visit: http://www.rand.org/pubs/research_briefs/RB5012/index1.html.

[3] **Evidence-Based Medicine.** See, for example, *Time,* June 19, 2009..

[4] ***New Yorker Article.*** Gawande, Atul. (2009). The Cost Conundrum: What a Texas town can teach us about health care. *New Yorker,* June 1.

[5] **End-of-Life Costs.** Austin, Bonnie G., J.D. and Lisa K. Fleisher (2003). Financing End-of Life Care: Challenges for An Aging Population. Academy Health is the national program office for HCFO, an initiative of The Robert Wood Johnson Foundation. Available on line at: http://www.hcfo.net/pdf/eolcare.pdf. See also: Liu K, J. M. Wiener, and M. R. Niefeld. (2006). End of Life Medicare and Medicaid Expenditures for Dually Eligible Beneficiaries. Health Care Financing Review, 27(4), 95-110 Available on-line at: http://www.cms.hhs.gov/HealthCareFinancingReview/downloads/06Summerpg95.pdf.

[6] **Fraud.** Fraud takes many forms. Some providers, for example, send in claims for treatments that never took place. Some suppliers take kickbacks for referring patients to particular companies. Some patients lend their ID cards to ineligible people and even sell drugs and equipment they received through the programs, e.g., wheelchairs. Texas is a leader in fighting Medicaid fraud: For a report on their efforts, visit:
http://www.hhsc.state.tx.us/OIE/Reports/2Half01SemiAnn_7dRpt.html.
See also: http://www.city-journal.org/html/16_2_medicaid_fraud.html.
http://www.fraudguides.com/tips/may23.asp,
http://www.omig.state.ny.us/data/content/view/25/52/.

Chapter 10: Empirical Rationing

[1] **Unsustainable Path.** Congressional Budget Office, July 17, 2009. Available on-line at: http://www.cbo.gov/publications/collections/health.cfm.

[2] **$483,000 per Household.** *The Economist,* June 13, 2009, p. 34.

[3] **Free-Market Rationing.** See the pioneering work in Fuchs, Victor. (1974). *Who Shall Live? Health, economics, and social choice.* New York: Basic Books.

[4] **Moral Hazard.** The idea that people insulated from risk will behave differently from those at risk: http://www.economist.com/RESEARCH/ECONOMICS/searchActionTerms.cfm? query=moral+hazard

[5] **Disabled.** See Briesacher, Becky, Bruce Stuard, Jalpa Doshi, Sachhin Kamal-Bahl, and Dennis Shea. (2002). Medicare's Disabled Beneficiaries: The forgotten population in the debate over drug benefits. Kaiser Family Foundation. http://kff.org/medicare/jupload/Medicare-s-Disabled-Beneficiaries-The-Forgotten-Population-in-the-Debate Over-Drug-Benefits-Report.pdf.

[6] **"Medicare for All."** See, for example, Singer, Peter. (2009). Why We Must Ration Health Care. *New York Times Magazine.* July 15, 2009.

[7] **Fewer than 45 Million.** The true number of uninsured Americans is the subject of vigorous debate. See, for a much smaller number: Cupp, S.E. (2009). Don't Be Fooled by Obama's "45 Million" Uninsured. FoxNews.com. July 21, 2009.

[8] **Certificates of Need.** For explanation, see: Shenkin, Henry A. (1996). *Current Dilemmas in Medical-Care Rationing: A pragmatic approach.* Lanham MD: University Press of America.

[9] **Formularies.** For Medicare's formularies and related regulations, visit: http://www.medicare.gov/publications/pubs/pdf/11112.pdf.

[10] **Cost/Effectiveness.** In the U.S., cost/effectiveness data are so far rarely used. Alternatives include Exclusion, Dilution, Deterrence, Delay, and Termination. See pp. 90-91 above.

[11] **Canadian Rationing.** See Dranove, David. (2003). *What's Your Life Worth?* Upper Saddle River NJ: Prentice-Hall. 49.

[12] **English Rationing.** See Dranove, David. (2003). *What's Your Life Worth?* Upper Saddle River NJ: Prentice-Hall. 52.

[13] **Oregon Rationing.** See Dranove, David. (2003). *What's Your Life Worth?* Upper Saddle River NJ: Prentice-Hall. Chapter 7.

[14] **Rationing Methodology.** For details, see Hadorn, David C. (1991). The Oregon Priority-Setting Exercise: Quality of life and public policy. *The Hastings Center Report, 21.*

Chapter 11: Clinical Rationing

[1] **"Rational" Rationing.** See Dranove, David. (2003). *What's Your Life Worth?* Upper Saddle River NJ: Prentice-Hall.

[2] **Preference for Clinical.** See Shenkin, Henry A. (1996). *Current Dilemmas in Medical-Care Rationing: A pragmatic approach.* Lanham MD: University Press of America. p. 25.

[3] **Rationing Techniques.** Klein, Rudolf, Patricia Day, and Sharon Redmayne. (1997). *British Medical Journal (BMJ), 314,* 7076.

[4] **Rationing Rule.** See Callahan, Daniel. (1987). *Setting Limits: Medical goals in an aging society.* New York: Simon and Schuster (Touchstone).

[5] **Affirmative Action Precedent.** See Purdy, Larry (2008). *Getting Under the Skin of "Diversity": Searching for the color-blind ideal.* Minneapolis MN: Robert Lawrence Press.

[6] **Rational Choice Theory.** For an introduction, see: http://www.britannica.com/EBchecked/topic/1069691/rational-choice-theory. For an alternative view, see: Herrnstein, Richard J., Howard Rachlin, and David Laibson. (1997). *The Matching Law: Papers in psychology and economics.* New York: Russell Sage Foundation.

Chapter 12: Ethical Issues in Rationing

[1] **Golden Rule.** For discussion of the Rule of Reciprocity, see: http://en.wikipedia.org/wiki/Ethic_of_reciprocity. See also Wattles, Jeffrey (1996). *The Golden Rule.* New York: Oxford.

[2] **Utilitarian Principle.** See, for Mill, http://plato.stanford.edu/entries/mill/; for Epicurus, http://plato.stanford.edu/entries/epicurus/.

[3] **Categorical Imperative.** See http://plato.stanford.edu/entries/kant-moral/.

[4] **Onerous.** How much is "onerous" is an empirical question that could be studied with standard social-science research methods.

[5] **Self-Destructive Behavior.** Herrnstein, Richard J., Howard Rachlin, and David Laibson. (1997). *The Matching Law: Papers in psychology and economics.* New York: Russell Sage Foundation, Cambridge MA: Harvard University.

[6] **Parallel the Abortion Debate.** An interesting theory in the euthanasia debate is that the implied right to privacy may protect the actor in euthanasia as it does in abortion.

[7] **Kant Opposed Suicide.** Kant himself argued that suicide could not turn into a general maxim because the self-love on which suicide is based could not both create life and destroy life when its continuation threatens more evil than it promises satisfaction. (Immanuel Kant, *Grounding for the Metaphysics of Morals,* pp. 30-31). We reply that voluntary euthanasia is qualitatively different from suicide, and that, in the situations we describe, life has effectively ended prior to the euthanizing. Our argument is parallel to the abortion debate: At what point does life begin, and at what point does it end?

[8] **Voluntary Euthanasia.** For a comparison of Switzerland's and Oregon's rules on assisted suicide, see:
http://www.allacademic.com/meta/p_mla_apa_research_citation/0/1/7/3/4/p17344_index.html
For a closer view of a Swiss organization that assists in suicide, see:
http://en.wikipedia.org/wiki/Dignitas_(euthanasia_group). See also:
http://www.cbsnews.com/stories/2003/02/12/60II/main540332.shtml.

[9] All but a handful of states have a specific prohibition against physician-assisted suicide. http://www.nightingalealliance.org/pdf/state_grid.pdf. Only Oregon permits it, although the citizens of several other states have petitioned for it.

Chapter 14: Affinity Groups

[1] **A Village.** See Clinton, Hilary Rodham. (1996). *It Takes a Village.* New York: Simon and Schuster.

[2] **Cities as Affinity Groups.** The Minnesota Legislature has commissioned a study of the benefits associated with designating "elder friendly cities." Chapter 60, House File 936 requiring the Minnesota Board on Aging to report on "communities for a lifetime."

[3] **Abuse.** "Abuse may need re-definition. If a patient and her Affinity Group view death as a normal part of life and prefer palliative care only, the revised definition of abuse should prevent the members and the organization from being sued civilly or charged criminally.

[4] **On the Job.** Benjamin, A.E., Ruth E. Matthias, Kathryn Kietzman, and Walter Furman. (2008). Retention of Paid Related Caregivers: Who stays and who leaves home care careers? *The Gerontologist, 48,* Special Issue 1, 104-113. See also: Kempter, Peter, Brigitt Heier, Teta Barry, Diane Brannon, Joe Angelelli, Joe Vasey, and Mindy Anderson-Knott. (2008). What Do Direct Care Workers Say Would Improve Their Jobs? Differences across settings. *The Gerontologist, 48,* Special Issue 1, 17-25.

Chapter 15: Individual Choices

[1] **Investments.** Both long-term care insurance and life insurance are insurance. We do not mean to imply that they are investments.

[2] **Young Versus Old.** See Westerhout, Ed W. M. T. (2006). Does Ageing Call for a Reform of the Health Care Sector? CESifo. Economic Studies 52(1), 1-31. Available on line at: Cesifo.oxfordjournals.org/cgi.content/abstract/52/1/1.

[3] **Physician-Assisted Suicide.** Carroll, Joseph. (2007). Public Divided Over Moral Acceptability of Doctor-Assisted Suicide. Gallup News Service. May 32. Available on-line at: http://www.gallup.com/poll/27727/public-divided-over-moral-acceptability-doctorassisted-suicide.aspx

[4] **Oregon's Death with Dignity Act.** The Oregon Act and annual reports can be found on line at: http://egov.oregon.gov/DHS/ph/pas/index.shtml.

[5] **Failed Efforts.** A list of states whose citizens have voted against legalizing physician-assisted suicide, visit: http://www.dredf.org/assisted_suicide/Failed_attempts.pdf.

Chapter 17: Grand Summary and Recommendations – Toward a National Conversation

[1] **Senators Kohl and Baucus.** Senator Herb Kohl and Senator entered into a formal colloquy on at-home and community-based healthcare services for older Americans. Visit: http://www.agingwashington.org/IlluminAgeApps/whatsnewApp/files/7B80AA312.pdf

[2] **Senator Kennedy.** Senator Edward M. Kennedy has introduced the CLASS Act, Community Living Assistance Services and Support, to create a national long-term insurance program. See http://www.medicalnewstoday.com/articles/158692.php.

[3] **$73 Billion.** Congressional Budget Office (2008), cited in Snyder, Sherry. (1998). Economic and Budget Outlook 1999-2008. Darby PA: Diane Publishing, Appendix G. See also: Total Medicaid LTC expense in 2006, $109 billion, of which 59% was for institutional care. Kaiser Commission on Medicaid and the Uninsured and Urban Institute analysis of HCFA/CMS-64 data (2006).

[4] **Marketplace of Ideas.** For history and discussion, visit: http://en.wikipedia.org/wiki/Marketplace_of_ideas.

[5] **Unintended Consequences.** Declining death rates increase long-term care needs as people live long enough to develop age-related conditions such as dementia, or live longer with existing disabilities. Stone, Robyn I. (2000). Long-term Care for the Elderly with Disabilities. Millbank Memorial Fund. http//:www.milbank.org/0008stone/.

[6] **Americorps**. For additional information, visit: http://www.americorps.gov/about/overview/index.asp.

[7] **Bankruptcy.** In 2000, half of the largest nursing-home chains filed for bankruptcy protection. . American Health Care Association. (n.d.). Nursing Home Statistics. http://www.efmoody.com/longterm/nursingstatistics.html.

[8] **Medicare Insolvent.** The Medicare trustees recently announced that the program will be insolvent earlier than anticipated, in 2017. See: http://www.kaisernetwork.org/daily_reports/rep_index.cfm?DR_ID=58435.

[9] **Medicaid Insolvent.** See *The Economist,* June 13, 2009.

[10] **Pigovian Taxes.** For Adam Smith quote, see: http://www.nytimes.com/2009/05/20/business/economy/20leonhardt.html. For definition, see: http://economics.about.com/od/incometaxestaxcuts/a/pigouvian_tax.htm.

[11] **VAT, National Sales Tax.** Montgomery, Lori. (2009). Once Considered Unthinkable, U.S. Sales Tax Gets Fresh Look. *Washington Post,* May 27, 2009. Available online at: http://www.washingtonpost.com/wp-dyn/content/article/2009/05/26/AR2009052602909.html.

[12] **Young versus Old.** See Callahan, Daniel. (1987). *Setting Limits: Medical Goals in an Ageing Society.* New York: Simon and Shuster (Touchstone). See also Chadwick, R., and M. Levitt. (1995). When Drug Treatment In the Elderly Is Not Cost Effective: An ethical dilemma in an environment of health care rationing. *Drugs and Aging,* See also: Shaw. A. B. (1996). Age as a Basis for Health Care Rationing: Support for agist policies. *Drugs and Aging.*

References

Traditional Sources

Aizenman, N. C. (2008). U.S. to Grow Grayer, More Diverse. *Washington Post,* August 14, p. A06.

Alzheimer's Association. (2009.) Alzheimer's Disease Facts and Figures. *Alzheimer's & Dementia,* Volume 5, Issue 3. alz.org/national/documents/report_alzfactsfigures2009.pdf.

American Health Care Association. (n.d.). Nursing Home Statistics. Available on-line at: efmoody.com/longterm/nursingstatistics.html.

American Health Care Association. (n.d.). Nursing Home Statistics. efmoody.com/longterm/nursingstatistics.html.

Austin, Bonnie G., J.D. and Lisa K. Fleisher (2003). Financing End-of Life Care: Challenges for An Aging Population. Available on-line at: hcfo.net/pdf/eolcare.pdf.

Benjamin, A. E., Ruth E. Matthias, Kathryn Kietzman, and Walter Furman. (2008). Who Stays and Who Leaves Home Care Careers?" *The Gerontologist, 48,* Special Issue 1.

Benjamin, A.E., Ruth E. Matthias, Kathryn Kietzman, and Walter Furman. (2008). Retention of Paid Related Caregivers: Who stays and who leaves home care careers? *The Gerontologist, 48,* Special Issue 1, 104-113.

Berkman, Lisa F., and Ichirō Kawachi. (2000). *Social Epidemiology.* New York: Oxford University Press.

Board of Trustees of the Federal Hospital Insurance and Federal Supplementary Medical Insurance Trust Funds. (2009). Annual Report.

Callahan, Daniel. (1987). *Setting Limits: Medical goals in an aging society.* New York: Simon and Schuster (Touchstone).

Cantwell, Michael F., Matthew T. McKenna, Eugene McCray, and Ida M. Onorato. (1998). Tuberculosis and Race/Ethnicity in the United States: Impact of socioeconomic status. *American Journal of Respiratory Critical Care Medicine.* 157(4), 1016-1020.

Carroll, Joseph. (2007). Public Divided Over Moral Acceptability of Doctor-Assisted Suicide. Gallup News Service. May 32. Available on-line at: gallup.com/poll/27727/public-divided-over-moral-acceptability-doctorassisted-suicide.aspx

Center for the Health Professions. (2006). An Aging U. S. Population and the Health Care Workforce: Factors affecting the need for geriatric care workers. University of California, San Francisco.

Centers for Medicare and Medicaid Services. (2008). Medicaid Spending Expected to Rise Must Faster than the Economy: Cumulative spending projected to reach $4.9 trillion over 10 years.

Chadwick, R.,, and M. Levitt. (1995). When Drug Treatment In the Elderly Is Not Cost Effective: An ethical dilemma in an environment of health care rationing. *Drugs and Aging,* addisononline.com/aging.

Clinton, Hilary Rodham. (1996). *It Takes a Village.* New York: Simon and Schuster.

Congressional Budget Office. (2003). Baby Boomers' Retirement Prospects: An Overview. Congressional Budget Office, November.

Congressional Budget Office (2008). See Snyder, Sherry. (1998). Economic and Budget Outlook 1999-2008. Darby PA: Diane Publishing.

Congressional Budget Office, (2009). Available on-line at: cbo.gov/publications/collections/health.cfm.

Crickmer, Amy. .(2005). Who wants to be a CNA? *Journal of Nursing Administration,* 35(9), September, 380.

Cupp, S.E. (2009). Don't Be Fooled by Obama's "45 Million" Uninsured. FoxNews.com. July 21, 2009.

Day, J.C. (2001) National population projections. U.S. Census Bureau. On-Line at: census.gov/population/www/pop-profile/natproj.html.

Department of Homeland Security. (2008). *Yearbook of Immigration Statistics.* On-Line at: dhs.gov/files/statistics/publications/yearbook.shtm.

Doyle, Kenneth O. (1999). *The Social Meanings of Money and Property: In search of a talisman.* Thousand Oaks CA: Sage.

Dranove, David. (2003). *What's Your Life Worth?* Upper Saddle River NJ: Prentice-Hall.

Economist. (2009), "Public Debt," June 13.

Ejaz, Farida K., Linda S. Noelker, Heather L. Menne, and Joshua G. Bagaka. (2008). The Impact of Stress and Support on Direct Care Workers' Job Satisfaction. *The Gerontologist, 48,* Special Issue I, 60-70.

End of Life Medicare and Medicaid Expenditures for Dually Eligible Beneficiaries. *Health Care Financing Review,* 27(4), 95-110 Available on-line at: cms.hhs.gov/HealthCareFinancingReview/downloads/06Summerpg95.pdf.

Fuchs, Victor. (1974). *Who Shall Live? Health, economics, and social choice.* New York: Basic Books.

Gawande, Atul. (2009). The Cost Conundrum: What a Texas town can teach us about health care. *New Yorker,* June 1.

Grunwald, Michael. (2009). How to Cut Health-Care Costs: Less care, more data. *Time,* June 23.

Hadorn, David C. (1991). The Oregon Priority-Setting Exercise: Quality of life and public policy. *The Hastings Center Report, 21.*

Herrnstein, Richard J., Howard Rachlin, and David Laibson. (1997). *The Matching Law: Papers in psychology and economics.* New York: Russell Sage Foundation, Cambridge MA: Harvard University.

Hwalek, Melanie, Victoria Straub, and Karen Kosniewski. (2008). Older Workers: An Opportunity to Expand the Long-Term Care/Direct Care Labor Force, *The Gerontologist, 48,* Special Issue I, 90-103.

Institute for the Future of Aging Services. (2007). The Long-Term Care Workforce: Can the crisis be fixed?

Kaiser (2004). See Kasper, Judith, and Molly O'Malley. (2007). Changes in Characteristics, Needs, and Payment for Care of Elderly Nursing Home Residents: 1999 to 2004. Kaiser Commission on Medicaid and the Uninsured. http//:kff.org.

Kaiser Foundation (2006). Fact Sheet. Washington D.C.: Kaiser Commission on Medicaid and the Uninsured.

Kaiser Foundation (2007). See Kasper, Judith, and Molly O'Malley. (2007). Changes in Characteristics, Needs, and Payment for Care of Elderly Nursing Home Residents: 1999 to 2004. Kaiser Commission on Medicaid and the Uninsured. http//:kff.org.

Kane, Robert L., and Joan C. West. (2005). *It Shouldn't Be This Way: The failure of long-term care.* Nashville: Vanderbilt University Press.

Kant, Immanel. (1785). *Fundamental Principles of the Metaphysic of Morals.* Abbott, Thomas Kingmill (tr.). Project Gutenburg e-book prepared by Matthew Stapleton.

Kasper, Judith, and Molly O'Malley. (2007). Changes in Characteristics, Needs, and Payment for Care of Elderly Nursing Home Residents: 1999 to 2004. Kaiser Commission on Medicaid and the Uninsured. http//:kff.org.

Kemper, Peter, Brigitt Heier, Teta Barry, Diane Brannon, Joe Angelelli, Joe Vasey, and Mindy Anderson-Knott. (2008). What do Direct Care Workers Say Would Improve Their Jobs? Differences across settings." *The Gerontologist, 48*, Special Issue 1, 17-25.

Kempter, Peter, Brigitt Heier, Teta Barry, Diane Brannon, Joe Angelelli, Joe Vasey, and Mindy Anderson-Knott. (2008). What Do Direct Care Workers Say Would Improve Their Jobs? Differences Across Settings. *The Gerontologist, 48,* Special Issue 1, 17-25.

Klein, Rudolf, Patricia Day, and Sharon Redmayne. (1997). *British Medical Journal (BMJ), 314,* 7076.

Komisar, H.L., J. Feder and J.D. Kasper. (2005). Unmet Long-Term Care Needs: An Analysis of Medicare-Medicaid Dual Eligibles. *Inquiry* 42(2): 171-182.

Liu K, J. M. Wiener, and M. R. Niefeld. (2006). End of Life Medicare and Medicaid Expenditures for Dually Eligible Beneficiaries. Washington D.C.: Health Policy Center, The Urban Institute.

Mongren, Randall, and Nancy Rytina. (2009). U.S. Legal Permanent Residents: 2008. Annual Report. Department of Homeland Security.

Montgomery, Lori. (2009). Once Considered Unthinkable, U.S. Sales Tax Gets Fresh Look. *Washington Post,* May 27, 2009. Available online at: washingtonpost.com/wp-dyn/content/article/2009/05/26/AR2009052602909.html.

Mutaner, C., Y. Li, X. Xue, P. O'Campo, H.J. Chung, and W.W. Eaton. (2004). Work Organization, Area Labor-Market Characteristics, and Depression among U.S. Nursing Home Workers: A cross-classified multi-level analysis. *International Journal of Occupational and Environmental Health,* 10, 392-400.

Ness, Jose, Ali Ahmed, and Wilbert S. Aronow. (2004). Demographics and Payment Characteristics of Nursing Home Residents in the United States: A 23-Year Trend. *The Journals of Gerontology Series A: Biological Sciences and Medical Sciences 59*:1213-1217.

Noelker, L.S., Z.Harel. (2000.) *Quality of Life and Quality of Care in Long-Term Care.* New York: Springer.

Pakula, Matthew (2005). The Legal Responsibility of Adult Children to Care for Indigent Parents. National Center for Policy Analysis, No. 521.

Passel, Jeffrey S., and D'Vera Cohn.(2008). *Trends in Unauthorized Immigration: Undocumented inflow now trails legal inflow.* Washington, DC: Pew Hispanic Center, October 2008. On-Line at: pewresearch.org/pubs/978/undocumented-immigration.

Purdy, Larry (2008). *Getting Under the Skin of "Diversity": Searching for the color-blind ideal.* Minneapolis MN: Robert Lawrence Press.

Secrest, Janet, Daniel H. Iorio, Wallis Martz. (2005). *The Meaning of Work for nursing Nursing Aassistants Who Stay in Long-Term Care."* New York: Hoboken N.J.: Blackwell Publishing (Wiley).

Senate Special Committee on Aging. (2009). Confidence in Long-Term Care Insurance Age of 2009,: opencongress.org/bill/111-s1177/show.

Shaw, . A. B. (1996). Age as a Basis for Health Care Rationing: Support for agist policies. *Drugs and Aging,* addisononline.com/aging.

Shenkin, Henry A. (1996). *Current Dilemmas in Medical-Care Rationing: A pragmatic approach.* Lanham MD: University Press of America.

Singer, Peter. (2009). Why We Must Ration Health Care. *New York Times Magazine.* July 15, 2009.

Snyder, Sherry. (1998). *Economic and Budget Outlook 1999-2008.* Darby PA: Diane Publishing, Appendix G.

Stone, Robyn I. (2000). Long-term Care for the Elderly with Disabilities. Millbank Memorial Fund. http//:milbank.org/0008stone/.http//AmericanCancerSociety.org.

Stone, R.I., and J. M. Weiner. (2001) *Who Will Care for Us? Addressing the long-term care worker crisis.* Washington DC: Urban Institute and American Association of Homes and Services for the Aging.

Time (2009). See: Grunwald, Michael. (2009). How to Cut Health-Care Costs: Less care, more data. *Time,* June 23.

U.S. Census Bureau. (2000). Projections of the Total Population of States 1995-2005: Population by selected age groups and sex: 1995-2005.

U.S. Department of Health and Human Services and U.S. Department of Labor. (2003). The Future Supply of Long-Term Care Workers in Relation to the Aging Baby Boom Generation. Report to Congress. Washington DC: Office of the Assistant Secretary for Planning and Evaluation. Available at http: aspe.hhs.gov/daltcp/reports/ltcwork.htm

U. S. Department of Labor. (2009). Quick Stats on Women Workers: 2008. On-Line: : http//:dol.gov/wb/stats/main.htm..

Van Den Eeden, Stephen K., Caroline M. Tanner, Allan L. Bernstein, Robin D. Fross, Amethyst Leimpeter, Daniel A. Bloch, and Lorene M. Nelson. (2003). Incidence of Parkinson's Disease: Variation by age, gender, and race/ethnicity. *American Journal of Epidemiology,* 157, 1015-22.

Vogel, Ronald J. (1999). *Medicare: Issues in political economy.* Ann Arbor: University of Michigan Press.

Waidmann, Timothy, and Korbin Liu. (2006). Analysis of HCFA/CMS-64 Data. Washington D.C.: Kaiser Commission on Medicaid and the Uninsured and Urban Institute (2006).

Wattles, Jeffrey (1996). *The Golden Rule.* New York: Oxford.

Westerhout, Ed W. M. T. ((2006). Does Ageing Call for a Reform of the Health Care Sector? CESifo. Economic Studies 52(1), 1-31. Available on line at: Cesifo.oxfordjournals.org/cgi.content/abstract/52/1/1.

On-Line Sources

agingwashington.org/IlluminAgeApps/whatsnewApp/files/7B80AA312.pdf

allacademic.com/meta/p_mla_apa_research_citation/0/1/7/3/4/p17344_index.html

alz.org/national/documents/report_africanamericanssilentepidemic.pdf

alz.org/national/documents/report_hispanic.pdf

americanheart.org/presenter.jhtml?identifier=4650.

americanheart.org/presenter.jhtml?identifier=4726.

americorps.gov/about/overview/index.asp.

archrespite.org/archfs54.htm.

blog.directcarealliance.org/category/direct-care-workers/and-turnover/

britannica.com/EBchecked/topic/1069691/rational-choice-theory.

cbsnews.com/stories/2003/02/12/60II/main540332.shtml.

cdc.gov/nchs/data/hus/hus08.pdf#026.

census.gov/population/www/socdemo/foreign/maps/TFB_Pntdist.pdf

city-journal.org/html/16_2_medicaid_fraud.html.

diabetes.org/diabetes-statistics/prevalence.jsp

dredf.org/assisted_suicide/Failed_attempts.pdf.

economics.about.com/od/incometaxestaxcuts/a/pigouvian_tax.htm.

economist.com/RESEARCH/ECONOMICS/searchActionTerms.cfm?query=moral+hazard

egov.oregon.gov/DHS/ph/pas/index.shtml.

elderlawanswers.com/resources/article.asp?id=3417§ion=4

ElderWeb.com.

en.wikipedia.org/wiki/Demographics_of_the_United_States

en.wikipedia.org/wiki/Dignitas_(euthanasia_group).

en.wikipedia.org/wiki/Ethic_of_reciprocity.

en.wikipedia.org/wiki/Marketplace_of_ideas.

everydaysimplicity.blogspot.com/2006/02/filial-responsibility-laws-list-of.html.

fraudguides.com/tips/may23.asp,

helpguide.org/elder/nursing_homes_skilled_nursing_facilities.htm.

helpguide.org/elder/respite_care.htm.

hhsc.state.tx.us/OIE/Reports/2Half01SemiAnn_7dRpt.html.

irs.gov/taxtopics/tc602.html.

kaisernetwork.org/daily_reports/rep_index.cfm?DR_ID=58435.

mayoclinic.com/health/long-term-care/HA00054

medicalnewstoday.com/articles/158692.php.

medicare.gov/LongTermCare/Static/Home.asp

medicare.gov/LongTermCare/Static/TypesOverview.asp

medicare.gov/Nursing/Alternatives/Pace.asp

medicare.gov/publications/pubs/pdf/11112.pdf.

mowaa.org/Page.aspx?pid=183

ncea.aoa.gov.

ncea.aoa.gov/NCEAroot/Main_Site/pdf/2-14-06%2060FACT%20SHEET.pdf.

ncpa.org/pub/ba521

nightingalealliance.org/pdf/state_grid.pdf.

nytimes.com/2009/05/20/business/economy/20leonhardt.html.

omig.state.ny.us/data/content/view/25/52/.

pewhispanic.org/states/population/

plato.stanford.edu/entries/epicurus/.

plato.stanford.edu/entries/mill/

pro.genworth.com/content/etc/medialib/genworth_v2/pdf/ltc_cost_of_care.Par.73347.File.dat/Summary%20of%20Findings_gnw.pdf.

pro.genworth.com/content/products/long_term_care/long_term_care/cost_of_care.html

publichealth.lacounty.gov/tb/facts/2005fact/2005Fact_Asian.pdf

rand.org/pubs/research_briefs/RB5012/index1.html.

tlchoices.com/experts/medicaid.asp.

tlchoices.com/finder/find-nursing-home.asp?CID=35.

tlchoices.com/hcfinder/

Appendix A: Excerpts from Oregon's Healthcare Priority List

http://www.oregon.gov/OHPPR/HSC/current_prior.shtml

Selected Disorders that *are* paid for, that is, above the cut-off

Rank	Disorder
453	Cancer of the Gallbladder, if greater than 5%, 5-year Survival
460	Trigeminal and Other Nerve Disorders (e.g., Facial Numbness)
461	Mal-union and Non-union of Fracture
462	Psychological Adjustment Disorders, including Bereavement
463	Hearing Loss over Age 5, including Hearing Aids
465	Atherosclerosis, Aortic and Renal
466	Macular Degeneration
470	Urinary Incontinence
474	Dental Conditions, e.g., Tooth Loss
476	Acute Bronchitis and Bronchiolitis
478	Obsessive-Compulsive Disorder
480	Anxiety Disorders
481	Osteoarthritis
482	Atelectasis (Collapse of the Lung)
483	Sensori-neural Hearing Loss Over Age 5
489	Chronic Sinusitis
492	Thrombosed and Complicated Hemorrhoids
493	Chronic Otitis Media
499	Dental Conditions and Severe Tooth Decay
502	Cervicitis and Other Inflammations of the Vagina

Selected Disorders that are *not* paid for (below the cut-off)

505 Broken Dental Appliances
506 Rupture of Knee Joint
507 Enophthalmos (Sunken Eyeball)
508 Corneal Inflammation due to Bell's Palsy
509 Peripheral Enthesopathies (e.g., Plantar Faciitis, Achilles Tendinitis)

510 Ringworm of Nail, Groin, or Foot
511 Conversion Disorder (Physical Paralysis from Emotional Causes)
512 Closed Fractures of Ribs and Sternum
515 Hepatorenal Syndrome (Renal Failure, Chronic Liver Disease)
518 Cerumen Impaction (Removal of Earwax)

520 Pink Eye
521 Joint Disorders
524 Nasal Cavity Disorders
526 Peripheral Nerve Disorder (as in Diabetes)
527 Closed Fracture of Big Toe

528 Tear Duct Disorders
529 Benign Kidney Tumor
530 Vertigo
531 Toe Fractures
532 Phlebitis, Thrombophlebitis

535 Vocal Cord Paralysis
539 Benign Nasal and Middle-Ear Tumors
540 Non-infectious Gastroenteritis and Colitis
543 Stomach and Digestive Disorders
545 Atropic Dermatitis, a form of Eczema

Appendix B: Recommended Readings

Callahan, Daniel. (1987). *Setting Limits: Medical goals in an aging society.* New York: Simon and Shuster (Touchstone).

A leading medical ethicist proposes answers to many of the most difficult rationing questions.

Daniels, Norman. (1985). *Just Health Care.* New York: Cambridge University.

A philosopher advocates healthcare justice through equal access.

Daschle, Tom. (2008). *Critical: What we can do about the health-care crisis.* New York: St. Martin's Press (Thomas Dunne).

The former Senate Majority Leader's prescription for American's ailing healthcare system.

Davidson, Stephen M., and Stephen A. Comers (Eds). (1998). *Remaking Medicaid: Managed care for the public good.* San Francisco: Jossey-Bass.

A collection of essays by leading theorists about Medicaid as managed care.

Dranove, David. (2003). *What's Your Life Worth?* Upper Saddle River NJ: FT Prentice-Hall.

Theory and practice of "rational rationing," the approach that underlies the Canadian, English, and Oregonian rationing systems.

Fleck, Leonard M. (2009). *Just Caring: Health care rationing and democratic deliberation.* New York: Oxford.

A philosopher urges society to make considered social healthcare agreements and to specify rationing procedures and priorities guided by social philosophers like Rawls and Dewey. He includes a critical assessment of competing healthcare reforms.

Hall, Mark A. (1997). *Making Medical Spending Decisions: The law, ethics, and economics of rationing mechanisms.* New York: Oxford University Press.

Exploration of who should make medical spending decisions, concluding that people need to understand more about how their health insurance affects medical spending decisions.

Kane, Robert L., and Joan C. West. (2005). *It Shouldn't Be This Way: The failure of long-term care.* Nashville: Vanderbilt University Press.

A physician and expert in long-term healthcare describes his family experience and advocates for fundamental change.

Kane, Robert L., R. Priester, and A.M. Totten. (2005). *Meeting the Challenge of Chronic Illness.* Baltimore: Johns Hopkins University Press.

Notable especially for its advocacy of improved information technology.

Morris, Dick, and Eileen McGann (2009). Obama Will Repeal Medicare. DickMorris.com, July 9, 2009.http://www.dickmorris.com/blog/2009/07/09/obama-will-repeal-medicare/#more-607

Fiercely partisan argument that Mr. Obama's healthcare plan will replace Medicare with a new government-managed rationing system that will short-change the elderly.

Shenkin, Henry A. (1996). *Current Dilemmas in Medical-Care Rationing: A pragmatic approach.* Lanham MD: University Press of America.

Early analysis of rationing as a response to soaring healthcare costs.

Singer, Peter (2009). Why We Must Ration Health Care. *New York Times Magazine.* July 19, 2009.

Sage arguments for rationing by the controversial Princeton ethicist.

Smith, David G., and Judith C. Moore. (2008). *Medicaid Politics and Policy 1965-2007.* New Brunswick NJ: Transaction.

Detailed history of the evolution of Medicaid told through interviews with major players in that history.

Ubel, Peter A. (2000). *Pricing Life: Why it's time for health care rationing.* Cambridge MA: MIT.

Internist and medical ethicist argues that we need to consider the cost/effectiveness of new medical technologies and think about not *whether* but *how* to ration healthcare.

West, John. (2009). *The Last Goodnights: Assisting my parents with their suicides.* Berkeley CA: Counterpoint.

Son recounts his experience helping both his parents end their lives.

Index

About the Authors

Ken Doyle is a financial psychologist on the tenured faculty of the University of Minnesota. A retired financial planner, he has held licenses in general securities, life/health insurance, and real estate, as well as psychology. He has a long-standing interest in the financial issues of the elderly. He studied philosophy at the Pontifical Gregorian University, Rome, and Marquette University, Milwaukee; and psychology at the University of Minnesota-Twin Cities, where he still teaches on the Strategic Communication faculty. Convener of the Minnesota chapter of the Circumnavigators Club and founding president of the Association for Financial Psychology, he is particularly interested in why people around the world do what they do with their money and property. He is author of *Wealth Accumulation and Management* and *Global Investing* (American Institute of Certified Public Accountants), *The Social Meanings of Money and Property: In search of a talisman* (Sage), and numerous other books and articles. He is the father of an adult daughter who is married and studying in Germany. His web address is www.KenDoyle.umn.edu.

Larry Houk is an attorney in private practice in Roseville, Minnesota, specializing in financial and estate planning for individuals and small businesses, particularly the legal and estate planning issues of the elderly. He holds a BA in Political Science from Bethel College, St. Paul, and a JD from the University of Minnesota Law School. A popular regional and national speaker on many legal and financial topics, he is author of *A Layman's Guide to Understanding Wills, Trusts and Probate* and co-author (with Ken Doyle) of *The Spend-Down Solution: How to deal with the financial and emotional costs of long-term healthcare.* He is married, the father of three adult children, and the grandfather of four. Accordingly, the topic of this book is of intense personal as well as professional interest. His web address is www.houkpa.com/.